Mindfulness
Puzzles

ARCTURUS

ARCTURUS

© 2017 Arcturus Holdings Limited
Puzzles copyright © Puzzle Press Ltd

ISBN: 978-1-78828-826-2
AD005775NT

Printed in the UK

2   4   6   8   10   9   7   5   3   1

CONTENTS

Introduction

We all spend far too much time thinking about the past, and worrying about the future, while the present is the only moment that we truly have. To be mindful simply means being in the present, awake to what we're experiencing right now.

Many studies have shown that living in the moment brings great psychological and even physical benefits. When we do something mindfully, and don't allow ourselves to be distracted by other thoughts, we do it better.

> ## "If you are depressed, you are living in the past. If you are anxious, you are living in the future. If you are at peace, you are living in the present."

Lao Tzu

Puzzling for mindfulness

Mindfulness is particularly well suited to solving puzzles. The act of completing one should be relished and enjoyed as a time to be in the moment, totally engaged in the puzzle in front of us, and free for a while from the distractions of everyday life.

Being mindful is a positive way to live our lives, and the more we do it, the more it becomes second nature. Solving puzzles is not only pleasurable in itself, it also helps to train our minds to be focused and engage with the task in hand.

> "Begin doing what you want to do now. We are not living in eternity. We have only this moment, sparkling like a star in our hand – and melting like a snowflake."

Francis Bacon 1561-1627

Making the most of mindful puzzling

While solving a puzzle is immensely satisfying, if we don't complete it in a mindful fashion we are missing out on some of its benefits. In order to be fully attentive to the task in hand, you may find it helpful to start by becoming aware of your breathing. Focus on the sensation as you breathe in, then as you breathe out. Breathe mindfully as you complete the puzzle too, taking time over it and allowing your mind to focus on how to solve it. You will find it easier to think clearly, and to enjoy the satisfaction of finding the answers.

Varying your routine

There may be puzzles in this collection of a kind that you already enjoy doing, if so, great! But trying something new, or breaking any pattern or routine, means that your mind is naturally forced to be in the moment. So don't be afraid to try a new sort of puzzle. Each type here is designed to be fun and engrossing, and you will find instructions to complete each throughout the book.

We hope you enjoy the puzzles in this book, and that they help you to achieve a mindful and relaxed state.

1   Wordsearch: Vegetables

Can you find all of the listed vegetables hidden in the grid below? Words run forward or backward, in either a horizontal, vertical or diagonal direction.

A	R	W	O	J	B	E	T	Q	A	N	E	B
R	E	P	L	X	L	U	M	J	B	E	S	I
K	P	V	R	Y	U	S	A	R	R	Z	C	Q
O	P	S	K	O	H	L	R	A	B	I	H	Y
S	E	P	I	N	R	U	T	T	G	A	A	K
H	P	M	U	S	H	R	O	O	M	M	L	N
K	V	Y	U	F	S	T	Q	D	R	U	O	G
G	K	P	S	D	I	J	D	M	M	R	T	U
C	Y	Q	O	P	D	R	G	V	O	E	A	G
E	G	G	P	L	A	N	T	F	G	G	D	C
O	L	S	A	H	R	R	S	E	A	W	Z	V
Z	L	A	C	R	E	S	S	N	R	V	U	T
C	G	D	K	G	O	Y	S	N	L	Q	K	Q
E	S	L	U	P	C	Q	K	E	I	Y	I	Y
B	C	U	U	O	P	L	O	L	C	P	P	Y

ADZUKI	GARLIC	PARSNIP
CARROT	GOURD	PEPPER
CHARD	KALE	PULSE
CRESS	KOHLRABI	RADISH
EGGPLANT	MAIZE	TURNIP
ESCHALOT	MUSHROOM	YAM
FENNEL	OKRA	

"We are awakened to the profound realization that the true path to liberation is to let go of everything."

Jack Kornfield

Arroword

Solve the clues, then enter each answer in the direction of the arrows, one letter per square.

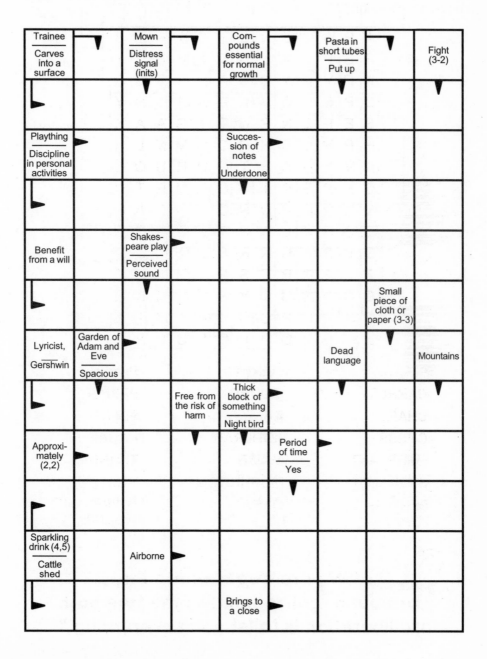

3   Criss Cross: Bees

The words are provided, but can you fit them all into the grid?

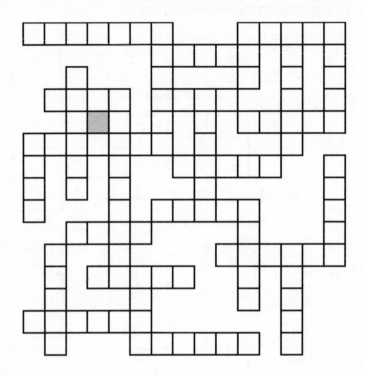

3 letters	FRAME	GARDEN
WAX	LARVA	GLOVES
	MITES	INSECT
4 letters	NESTS	NECTAR
COMB	QUEEN	SOCIAL
EGGS	SMOKE	
FOOD	SWARM	**7 letters**
PUPA	TREES	FLOWERS
VEIL	WINGS	HUMMING

5 letters	6 letters	9 letters
CELLS	COLONY	BEEKEEPER
DRONE	FLYING	

4   Domino Placement

A standard set of twenty-eight dominoes has been laid out as shown below. Can you draw in the edges of them all?

It may be helpful to use the check-box to tick off the dominoes as they are found.

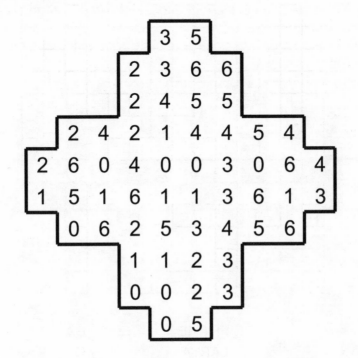

0-0	0-1	0-2	0-3	0-4	0-5	0-6	1-1

1-2	1-3	1-4	1-5	1-6	2-2	2-3	2-4	2-5	2-6

3-3	3-4	3-5	3-6	4-4	4-5	4-6	5-5	5-6	6-6

5   Codeword

Every letter in this puzzle has been replaced by a number, the number remaining the same for that letter wherever it occurs. Every letter of the alphabet has been used. Substitute numbers for letters to complete the codeword.

It may help to cross off the letters beneath the grid to keep a track of progress, and to use the reference box showing which numbers have been decoded. Three letters have already been entered into the grid, to help you on your way.

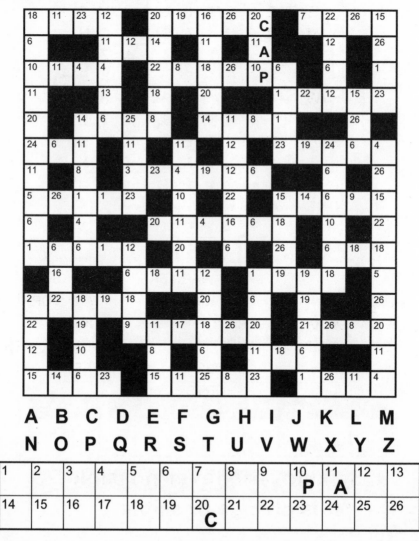

6   Wordsearch: Clothing

Can you find all of the listed items of clothing hidden in the grid below? Words run forward or backward, in either a horizontal, vertical or diagonal direction.

```
D V D E T A H R E L W O B
S U S H R X B B C V E S T
F S G T S E O H S S I V R
P R J S H B I M I R R P S
O E E E H G L S L P A M T
T M Z R A O I A S N S C N
K R X C J N R T Z A V Z A
N A S K C O S T C S R K P
A W R L D J N S S I A B R
T G P E U S R K B N N T E
B E F M H Z R E O G O D D
G L P I Z L Z R O L R H N
O E R Z J B A P T E P U U
R T M L E K Q P S T A X X
H S O T N I K C A M O L W
```

ANORAK	JUMPER	SINGLET
APRON	LEG WARMERS	SOCKS
BOOTS	MACKINTOSH	TANK TOP
BOWLER HAT	SARI	TIGHTS
BRASSIERE	SHIRT	UNDERPANTS
FEDORA	SHOES	VEST
JEANS	SHORTS	

"Be kind whenever possible. It is always possible."

Dalai Lama

7   Sudoku

Place one of the numbers from 1 to 9 into every empty cell so that each row, each column and each 3x3 block contains all the numbers from 1 to 9.

			2	9	5			
	2					8		7
3	4			7		9	6	
4			7			5	8	6
		2	9		6	7		
1	7	6			4			3
	3	9		4			2	5
8		7					4	
			6	1	9			

"Mindfulness is simply being aware of what is happening right now without wishing it were different; enjoying the pleasant without holding on when it changes (which it will); being with the unpleasant without fearing it will always be this way (which it won't)."

James Baraz

8   In Order

Nineteen pencils have been laid as seen below; each is marked with a different letter from A to R. Which letter denotes the pencil that was ninth to be placed on the pile?

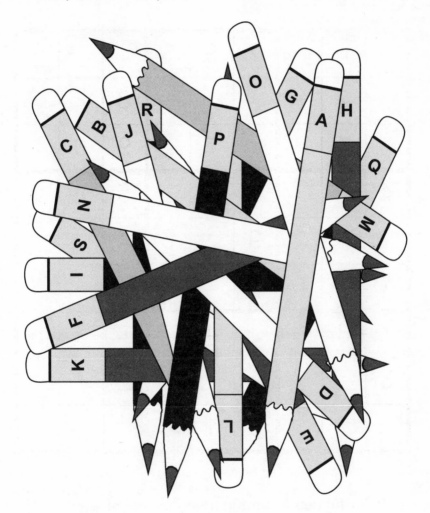

9   Word Wheel

How many words of three or more letters can you make from those in the wheel, without using plurals, abbreviations or proper nouns?

The central letter must appear once in every word and no letter in a section of the wheel may be used more than once.

There is at least one nine-letter word in the wheel.

Nine-letter word(s):

_____

10   Mind Over Matter

Given that the letters are valued 1-26 according to their places in the alphabet, can you crack the code to reveal the missing letter?

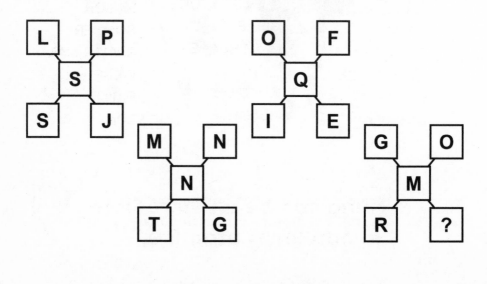

11 Wordsearch: Costume Party

Can you find all of the listed costumes hidden in the grid below?
Words run forward or backward, in either a horizontal, vertical or
diagonal direction.

```
T Q F L O W E R E W B E A
J W N B S I W K O F L N R
C O W B O Y M R G I N O V
H Q O P A Y P R L A F T S
W H L E U T E E M E N S T
I W C M Q I M E P A G T Q
T V H V D M C A M E R N I
C L O L U I F R N E O I A
H S O M L S E I S B L L B
Z S M O G D E A P E I F C
O Y P P I H T L V L A D I
M R S P O C K I R B S E Q
B R S R E P A E R M I R G
I N H U U D R N N U Y F A
E O I T O O F G I B F G S
```

ALIEN	FRED FLINTSTONE	POLICEMAN
ANGEL	GENIE	SAILOR
BATMAN	GRIM REAPER	SOLDIER
BIGFOOT	HIPPY	SPIDER-MAN
BUMBLEBEE	MR SPOCK	WEREWOLF
CLOWN	MUMMY	WITCH
COWBOY		ZOMBIE

"Writing can be an incredible mindfulness practice."

Jon Kabat-Zinn

12   Criss Cross: Bake a Cake

The words are provided, but can you fit them all into the grid?

4 letters	SPOON	RAISINS
EGGS	SUGAR	SPATULA
SALT		TESTING
TRAY	**6 letters**	
	GRATER	**8 letters**
5 letters	RECIPE	CURRANTS
CAKES	SPONGE	DECORATE
CREAM		SULTANAS
FLOUR	**7 letters**	
FRUIT	BEATING	**9 letters**
ICING	FILLING	PARCHMENT
MIXER	LOAF TIN	

Arroword

Solve the clues, then enter each answer in the direction of the arrows, one letter per square.

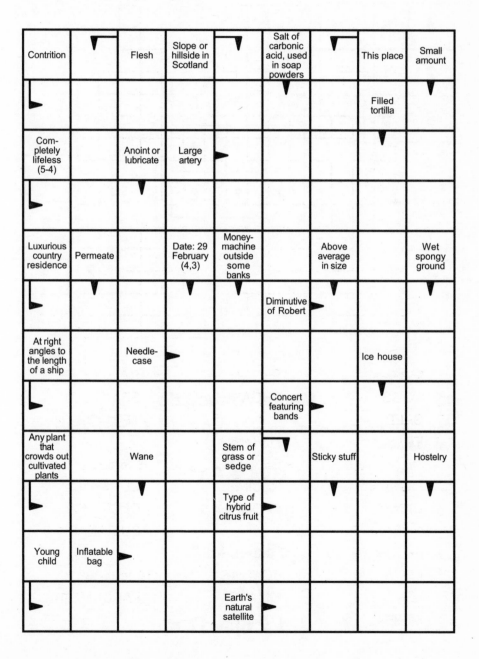

Contrition	▼	Flesh	Slope or hillside in Scotland	▼	Salt of carbonic acid, used in soap powders	▼	This place	Small amount
L					▼		Filled tortilla	▼
Completely lifeless (5-4)		Anoint or lubricate	Large artery	►		▼		
L		▼						
Luxurious country residence	Permeate		Date: 29 February (4,3)	Money-machine outside some banks		Above average in size		Wet spongy ground
L	▼		▼		Diminutive of Robert	►	▼	▼
At right angles to the length of a ship		Needle-case	►				Ice house	
L					Concert featuring bands	►	▼	
Any plant that crowds out cultivated plants		Wane		Stem of grass or sedge	▼	Sticky stuff		Hostelry
L		▼		Type of hybrid citrus fruit	►	▼		▼
Young child	Inflatable bag	►						
L				Earth's natural satellite	►			

14   Calculate

What number should replace the question mark in the central set?

4	6	7
2	1	3
8	5	5

7	9	8
7	?	6
9	7	8

3	3	1
5	8	3
1	2	3

15   **Mental Arithmetic**

Can you solve these sums in your head? The use of a calculator is not allowed!

$$304 \div 8 =$$

$$965 + 659 =$$

$$283 - 46 =$$

$$57 \times 7 =$$

$$(21 \times 6) - 17 =$$

16   Codeword

Every letter in this puzzle has been replaced by a number, the number remaining the same for that letter wherever it occurs. Every letter of the alphabet has been used. Substitute numbers for letters to complete the codeword.

It may help to cross off the letters beneath the grid to keep a track of progress, and to use the reference box showing which numbers have been decoded. Three letters have already been entered into the grid, to help you on your way.

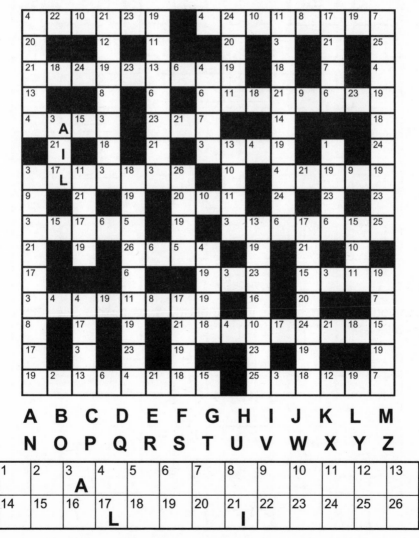

17   **Maze**

Find a path from one circle to the other through this maze.

18   Sudoku

Place one of the numbers from 1 to 9 into every empty cell so that each row, each column and each 3x3 block contains all the numbers from 1 to 9.

		4		2		3		
2	7		4		1		5	9
9			5		6			2
		2	8	7	5	1		
8	6						2	7
		1	2	6	9	5		
6			7		2			3
3	4		6		8		1	5
		9		5		6		

"If every day you practice walking and sitting meditation and generate the energy of mindfulness and concentration and peace, you are a cell in the body of the new Buddha. This is not a dream but is possible today and tomorrow."

Thich Nhat Hanh

19   Hexagony

Can you place the hexagons into the grid, so that where any hexagon touches another along a straight line, the contents of both triangles is the same? No rotation of any hexagon is allowed!

20   Total Concentration

The blank squares below should be filled with whole numbers between 1 and 40 inclusive, any of which may occur more than once, or not at all.

The numbers in every horizontal row add up to the totals on the right, as do the two long diagonal lines; whilst those in every vertical column add up to the totals along the bottom.

Can you discover the missing numbers?

								176
	40	6				21		203
18			4	11	16	9	13	97
24	8	1	8	38	10	12		138
19	35	33	27		25	14	4	160
38	29		34	6	19	15		202
15	25	34	33		12	38	29	220
	36	5	30	12	13	31	22	188
10	30	38	2		16			147
190	215	164	157	174	126	150	179	122

Number Cruncher

Starting at the top left with the number provided, work down from one box to another, applying the mathematical instructions to your running total.

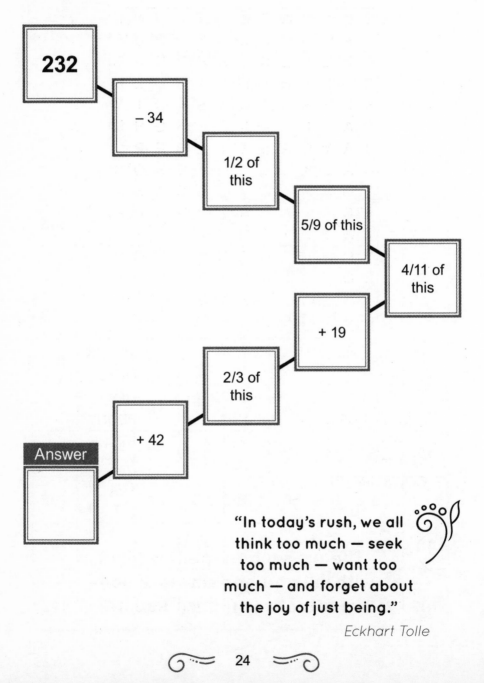

232

− 34

1/2 of this

5/9 of this

4/11 of this

+ 19

2/3 of this

+ 42

Answer

"In today's rush, we all think too much — seek too much — want too much — and forget about the joy of just being."

Eckhart Tolle

22 Wordsearch: Flowers

Can you find all of the listed flowers hidden in the grid below? Words run forward or backward, in either a horizontal, vertical or diagonal direction.

S	C	Y	N	W	D	W	F	Y	A	N	N	L
T	A	N	S	Y	R	U	S	I	U	P	U	L
O	L	E	F	E	C	I	K	R	D	R	A	E
C	I	F	T	H	A	R	D	I	S	U	L	B
K	L	S	S	D	A	Q	J	S	L	R	I	Y
G	A	I	L	L	A	R	D	I	A	G	H	R
J	A	Y	C	A	S	T	I	L	B	E	P	U
N	A	Z	K	O	G	X	G	I	U	R	O	B
T	G	S	A	A	W	Y	U	L	C	A	S	R
F	C	A	M	N	I	S	C	Y	M	N	P	E
J	W	T	S	I	I	N	L	L	J	I	Y	T
N	O	H	U	R	N	A	O	I	R	U	G	N
E	O	U	R	L	R	E	I	G	P	M	J	A
Y	G	S	W	I	I	Z	T	V	E	T	E	C
C	J	Y	N	O	E	P	Q	X	A	B	E	D

ASTER	DAISY	JASMINE
ASTILBE	FUCHSIA	LILAC
BEGONIA	GAILLARDIA	LILY
CANTERBURY BELL	GAZANIA	PEONY
CLARKIA	GERANIUM	STOCK
COWSLIP	GYPSOPHILA	TANSY
	IRIS	TULIP

"The present moment is filled with joy and happiness. If you are attentive, you will see it."

Thich Nhat Hanh

23   Sudoku

Place one of the numbers from 1 to 9 into every empty cell so that each row, each column and each 3x3 block contains all the numbers from 1 to 9.

7		5		2	9		4	
	2		3		5		1	
9							5	3
6		3	5	8				
		2	6		1	7		
				9	7	6		4
3	8				6			1
	4		7		6		2	
	6		8	4		5		9

"By breaking down our sense of self-importance, all we lose is a parasite that has long infected our minds. What we gain in return is freedom, openness of mind, spontaneity, simplicity, altruism: all qualities inherent in happiness."

Matthieu Ricard

Criss Cross: Horses

The words are provided, but can you fit them all into the grid?

3 letters	NEIGH	**8 letters**
BIT	PINTO	BLINKERS
	REINS	DRESSAGE
4 letters	SHIRE	PALOMINO
COLT		SKEWBALD
FOAL	**6 letters**	STIRRUPS
MANE	BRONCO	TROTTING
PONY	EQUINE	YEARLING
	HUNTER	
5 letters	WHINNY	**10 letters**
FILLY		CLYDESDALE
MARES	**7 letters**	
MOUNT	PADDOCK	

Coin Collecting

In this puzzle, an amateur coin collector has been out with his metal detector, searching for booty. He didn't have time to dig up all the coins he found, so has made a grid map, showing their locations, in the hope that if he loses the map, at least no-one else will understand it…

Those squares containing numbers are empty, but where a number appears in a square, it indicates how many coins are located in the squares (up to a maximum of eight) surrounding the numbered one, touching it at any corner or side. There is only one coin in any individual square.

Place a circle into every square containing a coin.

0		1		1			1	2	1
0			2		1		0		1
					1	2		3	
1			3						
				1	3		3		1
2		2							
				3		3	2		
2				6				3	1
	0					4			

"Calm mind brings inner strength and self-confidence, so that's very important for good health."

Dalai Lama

26   Codeword

Every letter in this puzzle has been replaced by a number, the number remaining the same for that letter wherever it occurs. Every letter of the alphabet has been used. Substitute numbers for letters to complete the codeword.

It may help to cross off the letters beneath the grid to keep a track of progress, and to use the reference box showing which numbers have been decoded. Three letters have already been entered into the grid, to help you on your way.

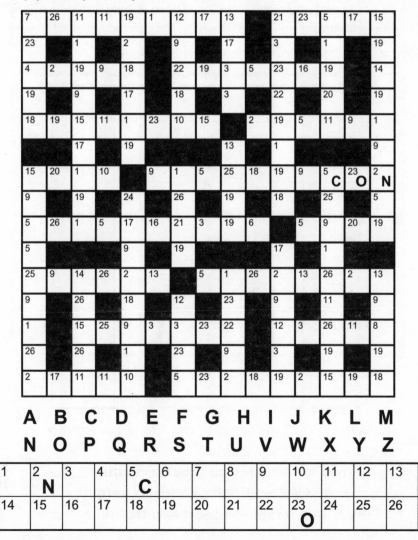

7	26	11	11	19	1	12	17	13		21	23	5	17	15
23		1		2		9		17		3		1		19
4	2	19	9	18		22	19	3	5	23	16	19		14
19		9		17		18		3		22		20		19
18	19	15	11	1	23	10	15		2	19	5	11	9	1
		17		19				13		1				9
15	20	1	10		9	1	5	25	18	19	9	5 (C)	23 (O)	2 (N)
9		19		24		26		19		18		25		5
5	26	1	5	17	16	21	3	19	6		5	9	20	19
5			9		19					17		1		
25	9	14	26	2	13		5	1	26	2	13	26	2	13
9		26		18		12		23		9		11		9
1		15	25	9	3	3	23	22		12	3	26	11	8
26		26		1		23		9		3		19		19
2	17	11	11	10		5	23	2	18	19	2	15	19	18

A B C D E F G H I J K L M
N O P Q R S T U V W X Y Z

1	2 **N**	3	4	5 **C**	6	7	8	9	10	11	12	13
14	15	16	17	18	19	20	21	22	23 **O**	24	25	26

27 Sudoku

Place one of the numbers from 1 to 9 into every empty cell so that each row, each column and each 3x3 block contains all the numbers from 1 to 9.

9	3	1	7					
		5		6	9		1	
2					1	8		4
1				7		9	8	
3			6		2			5
	6	7		1				3
7		4	8					9
	9		3	2		6		
					4	7	5	8

"Mindfulness has helped me succeed in almost every dimension of my life. By stopping regularly to look inward and become aware of my mental state, I stay connected to the source of my actions and thoughts and can guide them with considerably more intention."

Dustin Moskovitz

Arroword

Solve the clues, then enter each answer in the direction of the arrows, one letter per square.

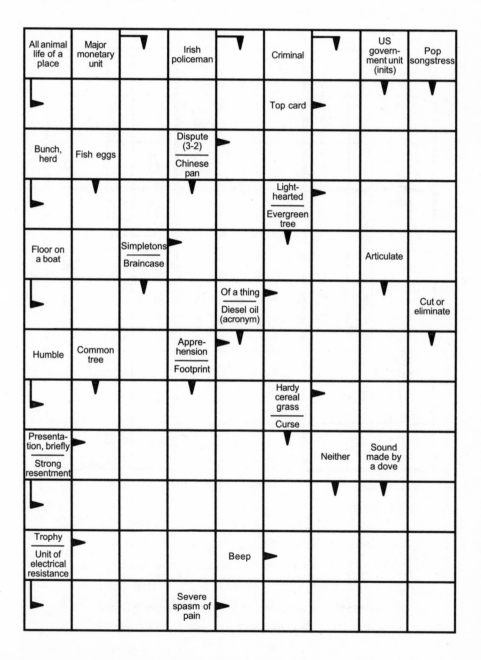

All animal life of a place	Major monetary unit	▼	Irish policeman	▼	Criminal	▼	US government unit (inits)	Pop songstress
⌐					Top card ►		▼	▼
Bunch, herd	Fish eggs		Dispute (3-2) / Chinese pan ►					
⌐			▼		Light-hearted / Evergreen tree	►		
Floor on a boat	Simpletons / Braincase ►				▼		Articulate	
⌐		▼	Of a thing / Diesel oil (acronym) ►				▼	Cut or eliminate
Humble	Common tree		Appre-hension / Footprint	▼				▼
⌐	▼		▼		Hardy cereal grass / Curse	►		
Presenta-tion, briefly / Strong resentment ►					▼	Neither	Sound made by a dove	
⌐							▼	▼
Trophy / Unit of electrical resistance ►			Beep ►					
⌐			Severe spasm of pain ►					

29 Wordsearch: Photography

Can you find all of the listed photography-related words hidden in the grid below? Words run forward or backward, in either a horizontal, vertical or diagonal direction.

```
N J P R E D E Y E M A T T
O C P J Q G L A Z I N G V
I L M B D B L U B L U R D
T O O O A Q N E J W M O E
A S D W E C U U N E Q E V
C E E I I R K D L S B O E
I U L M K O U G M O C D L
F P J Z Z L N T R F T A O
I H J E U A C T C O R X P
N C I P L H S O A I U L E
G B A K T B A S M J P N R
A S U B J E C T E F X I D
M N O C L S P S R T N H D
M Q D P V E E I A S D I E
M L I F I P Z B E J O V Q
```

ANGLE	DEVELOPER	MODEL
BACKGROUND	DODGE	PICTURE
BLUR	FILM	RED-EYE
BULB	GLAZING	RINSE
CABLE	LENS CAP	STROBE
CAMERA	MAGNIFICATION	SUBJECT
CLOSE-UP	MATT	

 "If you are doing mindfulness meditation, you are doing it with your ability to attend to the moment."

Daniel Goleman

30   Criss Cross: Jewels and Trinkets

The words are provided, but can you fit them all into the grid?

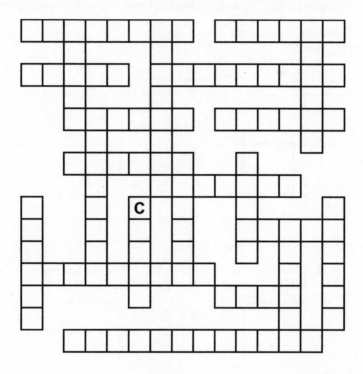

4 letters
CLIP

5 letters
CHARM
CLASP
CROWN
TIARA
WATCH

6 letters
ANKLET
BROOCH
CHOKER
COLLAR
DIADEM
HATPIN
LOCKET
PEARLS
TIE-PIN

7 letters
EARDROP

8 letters
EARRINGS
NECKBAND
NECKLACE

9 letters
CUFF LINKS
DRESS RING

12 letters
ETERNITY RING

31   Domino Placement

A standard set of twenty-eight dominoes has been laid out as shown below. Can you draw in the edges of them all?

It may be helpful to use the check-box to tick off the dominoes as they are found.

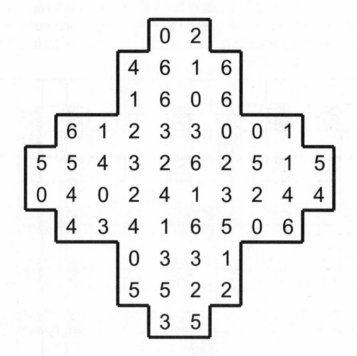

0-0	0-1	0-2	0-3	0-4	0-5	0-6	1-1

1-2	1-3	1-4	1-5	1-6	2-2	2-3	2-4	2-5	2-6

3-3	3-4	3-5	3-6	4-4	4-5	4-6	5-5	5-6	6-6

Codeword

Every letter in this puzzle has been replaced by a number, the number remaining the same for that letter wherever it occurs. Every letter of the alphabet has been used. Substitute numbers for letters to complete the codeword.

It may help to cross off the letters beneath the grid to keep a track of progress, and to use the reference box showing which numbers have been decoded. Three letters have already been entered into the grid, to help you on your way.

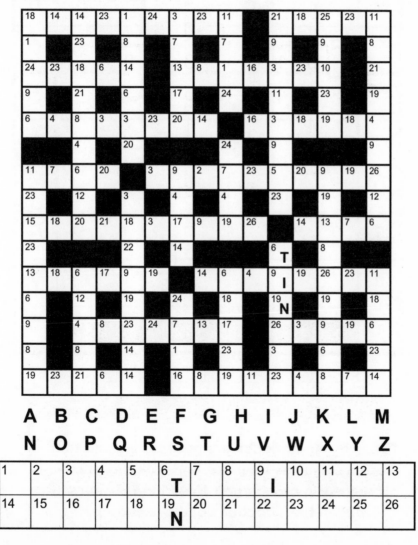

18	14	14	23	1	24	3	23	11		21	18	25	23	11
1		23		8		7		7		9		9		8
24	23	18	6	14		13	8	1	16	3	23	10		21
9		21		6		17		24		11		23		19
6	4	8	3	3	23	20	14		16	3	18	19	18	4
		4		20			24		9				9
11	7	6	20		3	9	2	7	23	5	20	9	19	26
23		12		3		4		4		23		19		12
15	18	20	21	18	3	17	9	19	26		14	13	7	6
23				22		14				6 T		8		
13	18	6	17	9	19		14	6	4	9 I	19	26	23	11
6		12		19		24		18		19 N		19		18
9		4	8	23	24	7	13	17		26	3	9	19	6
8		8		14		1		23		3		6		23
19	23	21	6	14		16	8	19	11	23	4	8	7	14

A B C D E F G H I J K L M

N O P Q R S T U V W X Y Z

1	2	3	4	5	6 **T**	7	8	9 **I**	10	11	12	13
14	15	16	17	18	19 **N**	20	21	22	23	24	25	26

Sudoku

Place one of the numbers from 1 to 9 into every empty cell so that each row, each column and each 3x3 block contains all the numbers from 1 to 9.

	4		5	6			7	
1			8					6
2	6	8				1	5	9
	3				6			5
		2	1		7	9		
9			4				8	
7	9	1				5	2	3
4					5			7
	8			3	2		9	

"The keys to patience are acceptance and faith.
Accept things as they are, and look realistically
at the world around you. Have faith in yourself
and in the direction you have chosen."

Ralph Marston

Eliminator

Every oval shape contains a different letter of the alphabet from A to K inclusive. Use the clues to determine their locations. Reference in the clues to 'due' means in any location along the same horizontal or vertical line.

1 The A is due north of the F, which is due east of the C.
2 The B is next to and west of the C, which is due south of (but not next to) the E.
3 The D is due north of the K, which is next to and west of the J.
4 The H is due north of the G, which is due west of the K, which is next to the I.

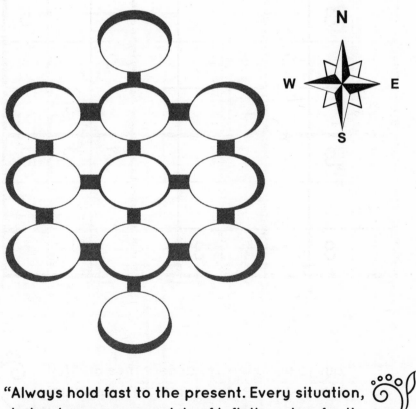

"Always hold fast to the present. Every situation, indeed every moment, is of infinite value, for it is the representative of a whole eternity."

Johann Wolfgang von Goethe

35 Maze

Find a path from one circle to the other through this maze.

Wordsearch: Hairdressing

Can you find all of the listed hairstyles hidden in the grid below? Words run forward or backward, in either a horizontal, vertical or diagonal direction.

```
N B O S Y N C U R L E D T
B P R I O I S I E A J O D
O E F E B C S Z W G P Y K
U R A D E B M O C K C A B
F M N Y G N S T N O L P R
F C A V A E E O R I O G A
A L W X P L T N A R A B I
N Z B L L V R T C Q B P D
T U A U Q O Y B U S R O N
N I M V W N E I P Z K N B
T F W S O E F T L H B U Y
H L E P H F R I Z E T T E
X O A I D E P M I R C O P
Z X V I M M A K O K L E B
F E E O S E N H Q E S W G
```

AFRO	CORNROWS	PERM
BACK-COMBED	CRIMPED	PLAIT
BEEHIVE	CROP	PONYTAIL
BOB	CURLED	QUIFF
BOUFFANT	FRIZETTE	TOPKNOT
BRAID	MULLET	WEAVE
BUN	PAGEBOY	

"Surrender to what is. Let go of what was. Have faith in what will be."

Sonia Ricotti

Arroword

Solve the clues, then enter each answer in the direction of the arrows, one letter per square.

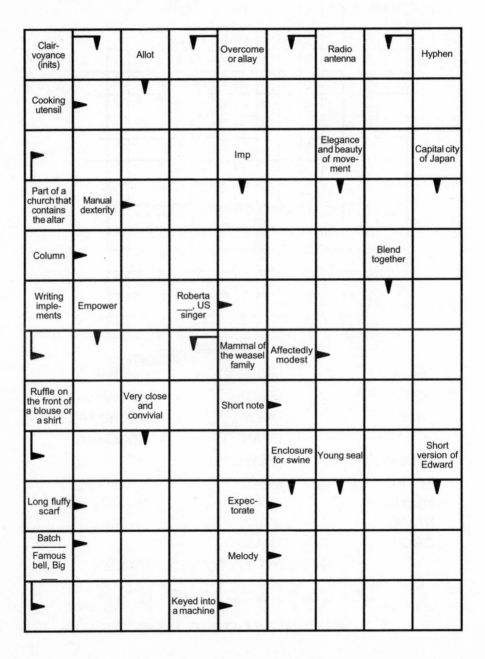

Criss Cross: Deserts

The words are provided, but can you fit them all into the grid?

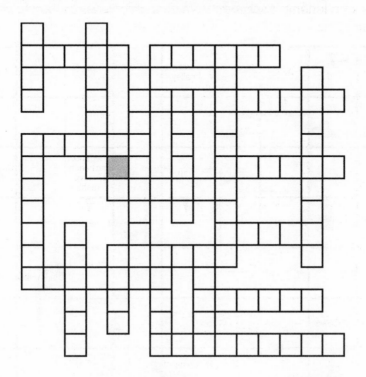

4 letters	6 letters	7 letters
GOBI	GIBSON	AL-DAHNA
THAR	JUDEAN	SECHURA
	LIBYAN	SONORAN
5 letters	MOJAVE	
KAVIR	NUBIAN	9 letters
MONTE	SAHARA	BLEDOWSKA
NAMIB	SYRIAN	LA GUAJIRA
ORDOS	TANAMI	

10 letters
AUSTRALIAN
PATAGONIAN
STRZELECKI

Starting at the top left with the number provided, work down from one box to another, applying the mathematical instructions to your running total.

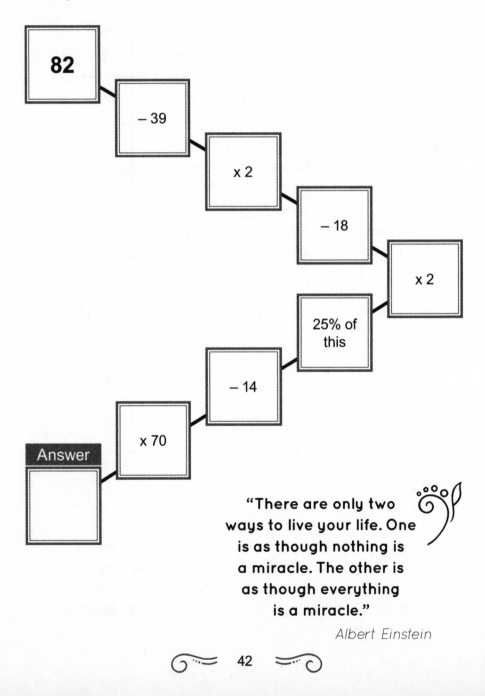

82

− 39

x 2

− 18

x 2

25% of this

− 14

x 70

Answer

"There are only two ways to live your life. One is as though nothing is a miracle. The other is as though everything is a miracle."

Albert Einstein

Sudoku

Place one of the numbers from 1 to 9 into every empty cell so that each row, each column and each 3x3 block contains all the numbers from 1 to 9.

	1	7				9		4
2	5			4	1			
	8	3		2				6
	6		7			1		
7		2	3		9	8		5
		8			2		4	
5				3		2	8	
			1	9			3	7
9		4				6	5	

"The practice of mindfulness begins in the small, remote cave of your unconscious mind and blossoms with the sunlight of your conscious life, reaching far beyond the people and places you can see."

Earon Davis

Hexagony

Can you place the hexagons into the grid, so that where any hexagon touches another along a straight line, the contents of both triangles is the same? No rotation of any hexagon is allowed!

42   Codeword

Every letter in this puzzle has been replaced by a number, the number remaining the same for that letter wherever it occurs. Every letter of the alphabet has been used. Substitute numbers for letters to complete the codeword.

It may help to cross off the letters beneath the grid to keep a track of progress, and to use the reference box showing which numbers have been decoded. Three letters have already been entered into the grid, to help you on your way.

9	21	16	6	23	9	■	7	20	5	5	24	6	12	6
21	■	12	■	16	■	2	■	12	■	16	■	12	■	3
23	6	8	24	21	■	19	11	6	9	5	1	11	16	25
16	■	19	■	16	25	19	■	21	■	24	■	20	■	19
12	6	25	■	18	■	23	19	9	11	19	5	21	19	3
8	■	6	■	6	■	■	12	■	6	■	16	■	25	■
19	9	5	24	16	25	1	21	■	11	16	23	5	19	25
■	16	■	6	■	13	■	6	■	6	■	8	■	26	■
15	20	16	4	19	23	■	5	16	21	24	1	25	6	5
■	12	■	19	■	6	■	19	■	■	16	■	16	■	16
22	16	23	23	16	5	20	3	16	■	13	■	12 (N)	6 (I)	11 (P)
19	■	19	■	25	■	12	■	26	1	14	■	1	■	6
19	17	11	25	1	9	6	10	19	■	6	9	25	19	21
5	■	19	■	20	■	18	■	12	■	23	■	6	■	16
24	1	25	6	3	16	13	9	■	4	19	23	12	19	25

A B C D E F G H I J K L M

N O P Q R S T U V W X Y Z

1	2	3	4	5	6	7	8	9	10	11	12	13
					I					**P**	**N**	

14	15	16	17	18	19	20	21	22	23	24	25	26

43   Total Concentration

The blank squares below should be filled with whole numbers between 1 and 40 inclusive, any of which may occur more than once, or not at all.

The numbers in every horizontal row add up to the totals on the right, as do the two long diagonal lines; whilst those in every vertical column add up to the totals along the bottom.

Can you discover the missing numbers?

								129
	17	40	25	15		30		187
23	6	13	26		29	38	11	167
32		27	22	12			6	128
	22		10	18	25		39	214
12	29	8		36	28	31		184
1	9	9	27	15	29	12		115
39	24	24	21			3	14	175
2	37	17		31	23	36	23	182
164	161	171	161	168	183	196	148	158

Sudoku

Place one of the numbers from 1 to 9 into every empty cell so that each row, each column and each 3x3 block contains all the numbers from 1 to 9.

7	5			2	4	8		
	4					7	9	
		2	9		7	1		
9	6		7	3				
2			6		1			5
			4	5			8	6
		8	5		6	2		
	9	3					1	
		6	3	8			4	7

"The best way to capture moments is to pay attention. This is how we cultivate mindfulness. Mindfulness means being awake. It means knowing what you are doing."

Jon Kabat-Zinn

45   Shape Up

Every row and column in this grid originally contained one circle, one diamond, one square, one triangle and two blank squares, although not necessarily in that order.

Every symbol with a black arrow refers to the first of the four symbols encountered when travelling in the direction of the arrow. Every symbol with a white arrow refers to the second of the four symbols encountered in the direction of the arrow.

Can you complete the original grid?

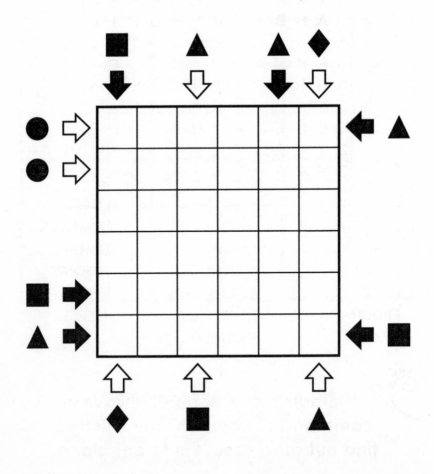

Wordsearch: Headgear

Can you find all of the listed items of headgear hidden in the grid below? Words run forward or backward, in either a horizontal, vertical or diagonal direction.

```
S G M H T W E L S A Y N C
O B H B N X F G F S B A Y
M T O R B F E A I J R W U
B A L A C L A V A W E Z E
R H N R T D C T R X D I T
E N T T X E Y E V N P U A
R I A K I A R M R K A R H
O A H B F L R P R Q C I P
A R A H R L L O Q O T M O
O R R G A U P A D V A O T
S H E T C I T H A E L I A
F S P L E P R I R X F I L
E E O R W F I N A H O O D
Z Y V Z W O Y T E R E B X
D F R A C S B Z H T A L L
```

BALACLAVA	FLAT CAP	SCARF
BERET	HAIRNET	SOMBRERO
BOATER	HOOD	TIARA
BOWLER	MANTILLA	TOP HAT
DERBY	OPERA HAT	TURBAN
FEDORA	PORK PIE	WIG
FEZ	RAIN HAT	

"Remain calm, serene, always in command of yourself. You will then find out how easy it is to get along."

Paramahansa Yogananda

Coin Collecting

In this puzzle, an amateur coin collector has been out with his metal detector, searching for booty. He didn't have time to dig up all the coins he found, so has made a grid map, showing their locations, in the hope that if he loses the map, at least no-one else will understand it…

Those squares containing numbers are empty, but where a number appears in a square, it indicates how many coins are located in the squares (up to a maximum of eight) surrounding the numbered one, touching it at any corner or side. There is only one coin in any individual square.

Place a circle into every square containing a coin.

			1		0			3
1	1							
2		2			0		3	4	
			3						1
	2		2			2	3	
		2						
	2	3				3		
	4		1	0				3
						3	5	
3			1				2	

"In the end, just three things matter: How well we have lived. How well we have loved. How well we have learned to let go."

Jack Kornfield

Criss Cross: Novelists

The words are provided, but can you fit them all into the grid?

5 letters
BOWEN
HARDY
MARSH
SCOTT
SWIFT
WOOLF
YATES

6 letters
ARCHER
BARRIE
HUXLEY
LEASOR
MARTEL
SAYERS
SEWELL

7 letters
BAGNOLD
BECKETT
FRANCIS
HERBERT
LE CARRE
MITFORD
RUSHDIE

9 letters
STEINBECK
STEVENSON

Tic-Tac-Toe

Place either O or X into each empty square, so that no four
consecutive squares in a straight line in any direction (horizontally,
vertically, or diagonally) contain more than three of the same symbol.

	O			X		X		O
			X			O		
X		X	O	X			O	X
					X	O	X	
	O	X		X	O			
		O				X	X	O
		X	O		X			X
O	X					X	X	
X		X		X	X	X		
X			X					O
O			O		O		O	
O					X	X		O

"The basic root of happiness lies in our
minds; outer circumstances are nothing
more than adverse or favorable."

Matthieu Ricard

50   Word Ladder

Change one letter at a time (but not the position of any letter) to make a new word – and move from the word at the top of the ladder to the word at the bottom using the exact number of rungs provided.

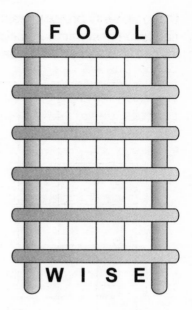

51   Word Wheel

How many words of three or more letters can you make from those in the wheel, without using plurals, abbreviations or proper nouns?

The central letter must appear once in every word and no letter in a section of the wheel may be used more than once.

There is at least one nine-letter word in the wheel.

Nine-letter word(s):

_____

52   Codeword

Every letter in this puzzle has been replaced by a number, the number remaining the same for that letter wherever it occurs. Every letter of the alphabet has been used. Substitute numbers for letters to complete the codeword.

It may help to cross off the letters beneath the grid to keep a track of progress, and to use the reference box showing which numbers have been decoded. Three letters have already been entered into the grid, to help you on your way.

12	5	8	19	21	18		25		13	14	14	13	20	8
8		12			5	11	21	12	11		6		3	
3	13	4	12	21	20		11		17		21		21	
13		15			6		16	4	12	23	24	21	11	16
4		5		7	24	12	2		2			8		4
	10	13	8	12		5		18		22	21	13	16	13
13				24	6	8	8	21	20	13		1		6
1	5	14	8	21		20		11		8	5	22	26	22
13		5		20	12	4	12	11 N	13 E	8 T				2
8	12	18	6	2		2		13		13	11	10	2	
21		16			6		8	4	13	13		13		8
20	4	13	18	21	8	12	4		11			9		3
	12		21		24		6		18	12	1	21	11	12
	8		11		6	11	21	22	13			11		4
8	6	7	13	4	22		8		18	4	6	16	12	11

A B C D E F G H I J K L M
N O P Q R S T U V W X Y Z

1	2	3	4	5	6	7	8 **T**	9	10	11 **N**	12	13 **E**
14	15	16	17	18	19	20	21	22	23	24	25	26

53   Arroword

Solve the clues, then enter each answer in the direction of the arrows, one letter per square.

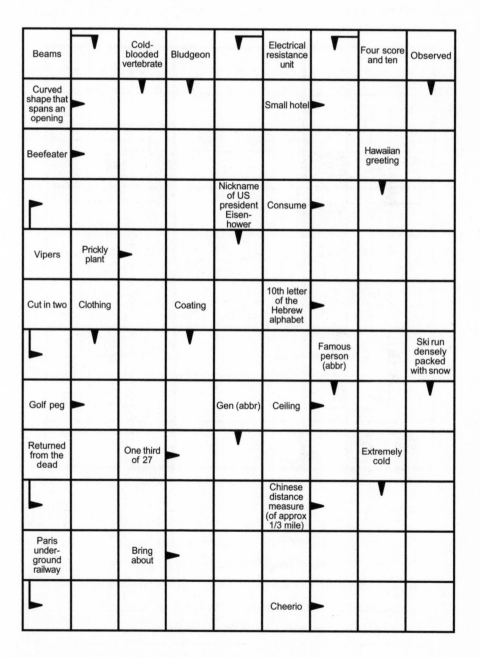

Sudoku

Place one of the numbers from 1 to 9 into every empty cell so that each row, each column and each 3x3 block contains all the numbers from 1 to 9.

				9	2		6	7
	4		5		1			8
9	5				7		4	
		9	7	6		2		
	7	6				1	5	
		3		2	5	6		
	2		8				9	5
7			2		4		3	
8	6		3	7				

"Mindfulness is the aware, balanced acceptance of the present experience. It isn't more complicated than that. It is opening to or receiving the present moment, pleasant or unpleasant, just as it is, without either clinging to it or rejecting it."

Sylvia Boorstein

55   **Wordsearch: London**

Can you find all of the listed words relating to London hidden in the grid below? Words run forward or backward, in either a horizontal, vertical or diagonal direction.

```
S O L I N E B G I B E L N
D D O L E G T M E K A O T
O N B D A V T E U M D C X
R S L O N M F K B N C L W
R C L L S E L E O Q E A C
A Y U Y A L T L F P N R S
H Y A T C H F S A P O E O
N B E A T O D H A P T N U
R R B N R Y C L H E A C T
U S C E K E S E I X P E H
B S W A T C U A R U H H B
Y O O I M D O P R O G O A
T X H L F D A C S K S U N
O W O I B P E U U W B S K
D J S E R P E N T I N E N
```

BEEFEATER	COCKNEY	PALL MALL
BIG BEN	CUTTY SARK	SERPENTINE
CABS	EAST END	SOHO
CAMDEN	EROS	SOUTH BANK
CENOTAPH	GUILDHALL	TOWER OF
CLARENCE	HARRODS	LONDON
HOUSE	LAMBETH	TYBURN
		WHITECHAPEL

"If you want others to be happy, practice compassion. If you want to be happy, practice compassion."

Dalai Lama

56   Criss Cross: Mountains

The words are provided, but can you fit them all into the grid?

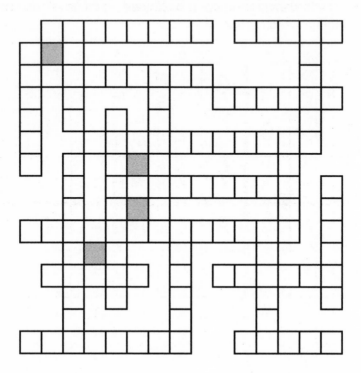

5 letters
ADAMS
CENIS
HEKLA
JANNU
KAMET

6 letters
ARARAT
CARMEL
GONGGA
MAKALU

NUPTSE
TALUNG
VINSON

8 letters
CHANGTSE
MCKINLEY
RUSHMORE

9 letters
ACONCAGUA
ANNAPURNA

BROAD PEAK
KAMBACHEN

11 letters
MACHU PICCHU

13 letters
KANGCHEN-
JUNGA

Sudoku

Place one of the numbers from 1 to 9 into every empty cell so that each row, each column and each 3x3 block contains all the numbers from 1 to 9.

			6		5			1
5	7	6		8				2
			7	2	4			5
		8	9		3		4	
9	3						1	6
	4		1		8	5		
4			5	3	7			
2				1		9	7	4
8			2		9			

"Acceptance looks like a passive state, but in reality it brings something entirely new into this world. That peace, a subtle energy vibration, is consciousness."

Eckhart Tolle

58 Wordsearch: Baseball

Can you find all of the listed baseball terms hidden in the grid below? Words run forward or backward, in either a horizontal, vertical or diagonal direction.

```
Y M E E L J M E S T C B U
J J K N X B D I D T E A M
O B I N N I N G I L N B P
P M R O E G J X B R A X I
U E T V L R U U Y S S B R
E T S E P V O X E C U C E
G A J C I D K S A L U O F
N L W O R H T T E R J C Z
A P O U T P C B V S S A Q
H S U V R H G E B E A L B
C X Q K E S B S J K G L S
D B Z R B A T T E R W T C
Q Z A C L H N E O H I P I
O W A L K T M A H H F S T
G T R Z K Y T L X C S P L
```

BALK	FOUL	STRIKE
BASES	GLOVE	TEAM
BATTER	HITS	THROW
CATCHER	INNING	TRIPLE
CHANGE UP	PLATE	UMPIRE
CURVE BALL	SINGLE	WALK
DOUBLE	STEAL	

"The ideal of calm exists in a sitting cat."

Jules Renard

59 Codeword

Every letter in this puzzle has been replaced by a number, the number remaining the same for that letter wherever it occurs. Every letter of the alphabet has been used. Substitute numbers for letters to complete the codeword.

It may help to cross off the letters beneath the grid to keep a track of progress, and to use the reference box showing which numbers have been decoded. Three letters have already been entered into the grid, to help you on your way.

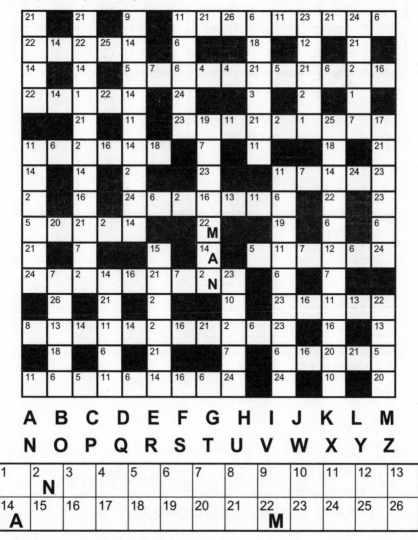

A B C D E F G H I J K L M
N O P Q R S T U V W X Y Z

1	2 N	3	4	5	6	7	8	9	10	11	12	13
14 A	15	16	17	18	19	20	21	22 M	23	24	25	26

Sudoku

Place one of the numbers from 1 to 9 into every empty cell so that each row, each column and each 3x3 block contains all the numbers from 1 to 9.

	4		2	1		5		3
	2	7				6		
	1		9		4		8	
				5	9	1		4
8			4		6			9
7		4	3	2				
	8		7		3		6	
		5				7	3	
3		9		8	5		1	

"Mindfulness is about love and loving life. When you cultivate this love, it gives you clarity and compassion for life, and your actions happen in accordance with that."

Jon Kabat-Zinn

61   Domino Placement

A standard set of twenty-eight dominoes has been laid out as shown below. Can you draw in the edges of them all?

It may be helpful to use the check-box to tick off the dominoes as they are found.

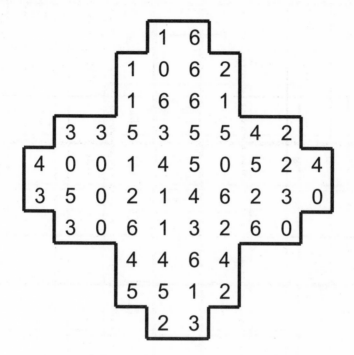

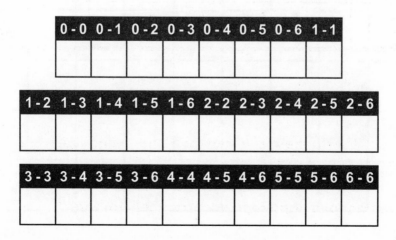

0-0	0-1	0-2	0-3	0-4	0-5	0-6	1-1

1-2	1-3	1-4	1-5	1-6	2-2	2-3	2-4	2-5	2-6

3-3	3-4	3-5	3-6	4-4	4-5	4-6	5-5	5-6	6-6

Arroword

Solve the clues, then enter each answer in the direction of the arrows, one letter per square.

Expend	▼	Country, capital Lilongwe	▼	Giant	Shun	▼	Barrier constructed to keep out the sea	Unspecified object or degree
Emoticon of a grinning face ►		▼			▼		Imprudent, talkative	▼
⚑				Largest organ of the body ►			▼	
Vegetable matter used as a fuel	Theft ►							
⚑				Leaves in order to join an opposing cause		Through		Give permission to
Long-necked bird	Communist state of Asia		Evil spirit ►	▼		▼		▼
Similarly ►	▼							
Bestow		Bird's home	Exploit		Pretend ►			
◤		▼	▼			H Rider Haggard novel		Wing of an insect
Oracle ►				Division of an ocean ►		▼		▼
Lightly strikes a golf ball	Schoolbag ►							
◤				Hour at which something is due (inits) ►				

63   Wordsearch: Setting a Table

Can you find all of the listed words hidden in the grid below? Words run forward or backward, in either a horizontal, vertical or diagonal direction.

```
M A T W D C D P L J J F Y
O J O A Q W E W N D W D S
B X E T O P O T G J V T T
X R M S P B P D G T N Q H
B Z V E T U Y U F E P T N
E T R I H E J V M O O N O
D L U C N R A I A L R X O
X R T R E E D K C R X K P
F E A T E N G E K K G C S
K L A T O E L A D N N N A
Y W O C S B N E R I I R E
S Q X W A U E C U V K F T
A S V T E I M N R E P D E
L A D L E R I W I S A R M
T V Z K M E S Y M W N R S
```

BREAD	KNIVES	TABLECLOTH
CONDIMENTS	LADLE	TEASPOON
FLOWERS	MUSTARD	TUREEN
FORKS	NAPKIN	VINEGAR
FRUIT BOWL	PEPPER	WATER JUG
GRAVY BOAT	SALT	WINE BOTTLE
KETCHUP	STEAK KNIFE	

"Things falling apart is a kind of testing and also a kind of healing."

Pema Chodron

64   Round Up

The number in each circle is the sum of the two numbers below it. Just work out the missing numbers in every circle!

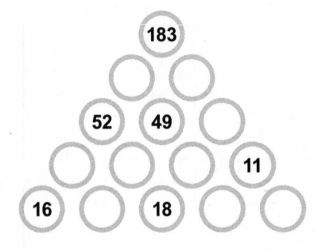

65   Round Numbers

Fill the circles so that every horizontal row and vertical column of six circles contains the numbers 1-6 inclusive. The shaded circles contain odd numbers 1, 3 and 5, and the white circles contain even numbers 2, 4 and 6. Some numbers are already in place.

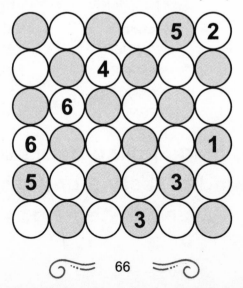

Criss Cross: "K" Words

The words are provided, but can you fit them all into the grid?

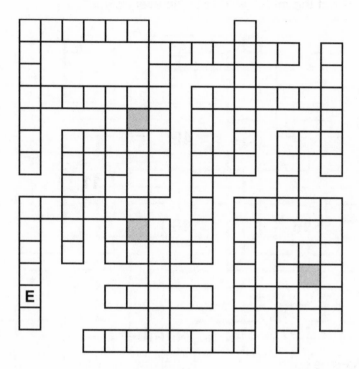

3 letters
KEG
KIP
KIT

4 letters
KELP

5 letters
KAPOK
KHAKI
KNAVE
KNIFE

KOALA
KRILL

6 letters
KANSAS
KARATE
KAYAKS
KEENLY
KILLER
KIMONO
KIPPER

7 letters
KASHMIR
KEELING
KICKING
KIDDING
KISSING
KNOCKED
KNUCKLE

8 letters
KEYSTONE
KNAPSACK
KRAKATOA

67 Maze

Find a path from one circle to the other through this maze.

Codeword

Every letter in this puzzle has been replaced by a number, the number remaining the same for that letter wherever it occurs. Every letter of the alphabet has been used. Substitute numbers for letters to complete the codeword.

It may help to cross off the letters beneath the grid to keep a track of progress, and to use the reference box showing which numbers have been decoded. Three letters have already been entered into the grid, to help you on your way.

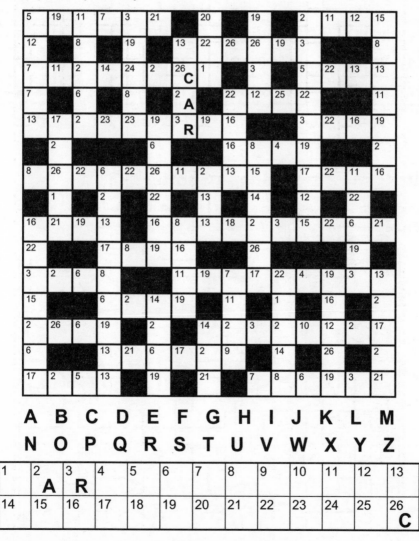

A B C D E F G H I J K L M
N O P Q R S T U V W X Y Z

1	2 A	3 R	4	5	6	7	8	9	10	11	12	13
14	15	16	17	18	19	20	21	22	23	24	25	26 C

69   **Whatever Next?**

Which of the four lettered alternatives (A, B, C or D) fits most logically into the empty square?

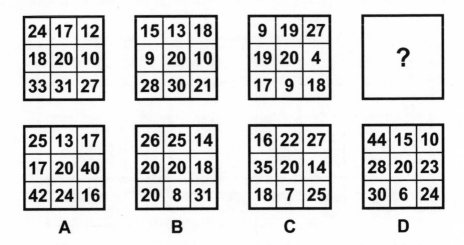

24	17	12
18	20	10
33	31	27

15	13	18
9	20	10
28	30	21

9	19	27
19	20	4
17	9	18

?

25	13	17
17	20	40
42	24	16

A

26	25	14
20	20	18
20	8	31

B

16	22	27
35	20	14
18	7	25

C

44	15	10
28	20	23
30	6	24

D

70   **Shape Spotter**

Which is the only shape to appear twice in the box below? You'll need a keen eye for this one, as some shapes overlap others!

Sudoku

Place one of the numbers from 1 to 9 into every empty cell so that each row, each column and each 3x3 block contains all the numbers from 1 to 9.

9	6				2		5	7
4		7	3			6		2
2				7				8
	2	4		6	5			
		9				5		
			1	8		2	3	
8				4				3
7		3			9	1		5
6	1		7				8	4

"Drink your tea slowly and reverently, as if it
is the axis on which the world earth revolves —
slowly, evenly, without rushing toward the future;
live the actual moment. Only this moment is life."

Thich Nhat Hanh

Hexagony

Can you place the hexagons into the grid, so that where any hexagon touches another along a straight line, the contents of both triangles is the same? No rotation of any hexagon is allowed!

73   Total Concentration

The blank squares below should be filled with whole numbers between 1 and 40 inclusive, any of which may occur more than once, or not at all.

The numbers in every horizontal row add up to the totals on the right, as do the two long diagonal lines; whilst those in every vertical column add up to the totals along the bottom.

Can you discover the missing numbers?

								115
33	11	37		23		22	2	164
21	18		31		13	13	39	167
32	35	25		24	11	21	19	203
6		29	31			26	18	186
38	24	39		18	22		23	213
	3	8	15		11	10	28	131
	9	20	29	22	19			161
13	12	35	24		39	29	31	221
188	145	202	213	208	152	150	188	179

Wordsearch: Bible Characters

Can you find all of the listed names hidden in the grid below? Words run forward or backward, in either a horizontal, vertical or diagonal direction.

```
B K P F A N N A O J J W K
O D I V A D O N Y U E W O
A R R Z Z N H R E R J F F
Z P A R R O I Y A I D E U
B Q V X J X I X S A Z O B
F I R T A L C H N H Y J K
C Y R U S E A J W M A R Y
R A O E G C L B B Q N Q Y
O X R E H O B O A M O E D
L D Y U S C Q H B N E O K
P E H O S E A W E R D N A
Q N A U U F N N C A I J L
S H W J I M O A N Q G K A
V J E Z E B E L X E J O B
R P F X Z V M O L A S B A
```

AARON	GIDEON	LABAN
ABSALOM	HOSEA	MARY
ANDREW	JAEL	NAOMI
BALAK	JEZEBEL	REHOBOAM
BOAZ	JOANNA	SENNACHERIB
CYRUS	JOB	URIAH
DAVID	JOHN	

"Begin at once to live, and count each separate day as a separate life."

Seneca

Criss Cross: Animals' Homes

The words are provided, but can you fit them all into the grid?

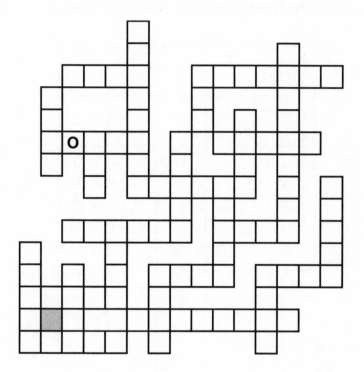

3 letters
DEN
PEN

4 letters
BYRE
CAVE
COOP
DREY
FOLD
HOLT
LAIR
NEST

SETT
STUD

5 letters
EARTH
EYRIE
HUTCH
LEDGE
LODGE
MOUND
ROOST
STALL

6 letters
KENNEL
STABLE

7 letters
PADDOCK

8 letters
DOVECOTE
FORTRESS

9 letters
FORMICARY

Arroword

Solve the clues, then enter each answer in the direction of the arrows, one letter per square.

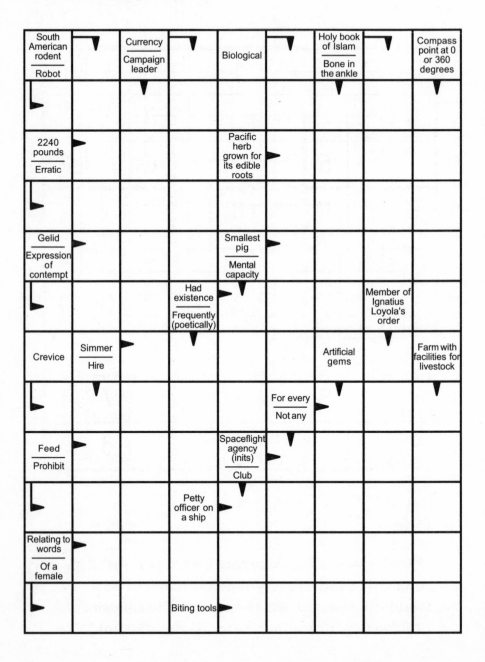

Sudoku

Place one of the numbers from 1 to 9 into every empty cell so that each row, each column and each 3x3 block contains all the numbers from 1 to 9.

	2		5	1				7
8	1		4			3		
		5			7	6		8
6	4	9	1	8				
7								2
				3	4	8	6	9
5		4	2			9		
		8			3		7	1
9				6	5		3	

"Mindfulness is a quality that's always there. It's an illusion that there's a meditation and post-meditation period, which I always find amusing, because you're either mindful or you're not."

Richard Gere

78   Codeword

Every letter in this puzzle has been replaced by a number, the number remaining the same for that letter wherever it occurs. Every letter of the alphabet has been used. Substitute numbers for letters to complete the codeword.

It may help to cross off the letters beneath the grid to keep a track of progress, and to use the reference box showing which numbers have been decoded. Three letters have already been entered into the grid, to help you on your way.

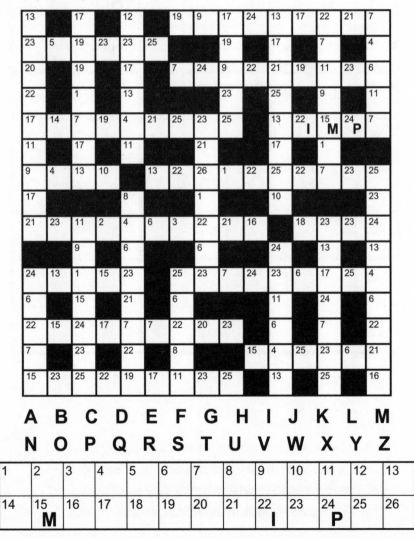

A B C D E F G H I J K L M

N O P Q R S T U V W X Y Z

1	2	3	4	5	6	7	8	9	10	11	12	13
14	15 **M**	16	17	18	19	20	21	22 **I**	23	24 **P**	25	26

Eliminator

Every oval shape contains a different letter of the alphabet from A to K inclusive. Use the clues to determine their locations. Reference in the clues to 'due' means in any location along the same horizontal or vertical line.

1   The A is next to and north of the H, which is next to and east of the J.
2   The B is next to and west of the I, which is next to and north of the K.
3   The C is next to and west of the D, which is further north than the J.
4   The E is further south than the F, but further north than the G (which is further north than the K).

"I wish that life should not be cheap, but sacred. I wish the days to be as centuries, loaded, fragrant."

Ralph Waldo Emerson

Sudoku

Place one of the numbers from 1 to 9 into every empty cell so that each row, each column and each 3x3 block contains all the numbers from 1 to 9.

8	2	6		4		9		
			2		6	5		
			8	9	7	6		
	4		3		1			7
1		3				2		5
7			5		4		6	
		7	6	1	8			
		4	9		3			
		9		5		7	3	8

"Mindfulness is often spoken of as the heart of Buddhist meditation. It's not about Buddhism, but about paying attention. That's what all meditation is, no matter what tradition or particular technique is used."

Jon Kabat-Zinn

81   Coin Collecting

In this puzzle, an amateur coin collector has been out with his metal detector, searching for booty. He didn't have time to dig up all the coins he found, so has made a grid map, showing their locations, in the hope that if he loses the map, at least no-one else will understand it…

Those squares containing numbers are empty, but where a number appears in a square, it indicates how many coins are located in the squares (up to a maximum of eight) surrounding the numbered one, touching it at any corner or side. There is only one coin in any individual square.

Place a circle into every square containing a coin.

	0				1	2			
				2				1	
1		1				2		3	
				1		1			
	0		1				2	4	
2				4			3		
					5				
		2			4			3	
	3			2				0	
1		1			1		1		

"We must go beyond the constant clamor of ego, beyond the tools of logic and reason, to the still, calm place within us: the realm of the soul."

Deepak Chopra

Number Cruncher

Starting at the top left with the number provided, work down from one box to another, applying the mathematical instructions to your running total.

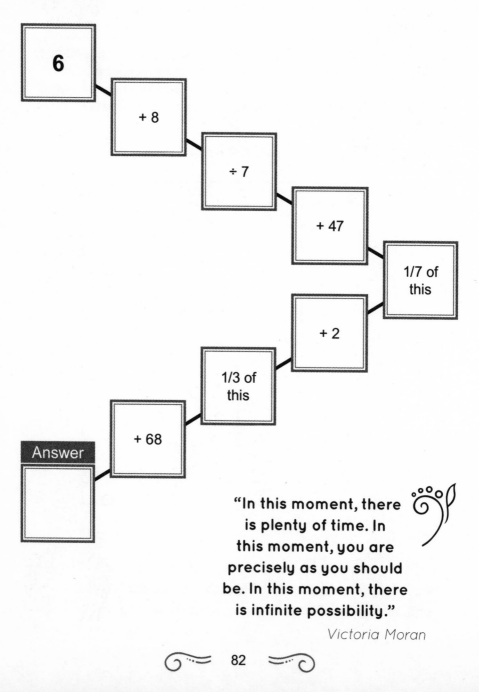

6

+ 8

÷ 7

+ 47

1/7 of this

+ 2

1/3 of this

+ 68

Answer

"In this moment, there is plenty of time. In this moment, you are precisely as you should be. In this moment, there is infinite possibility."

Victoria Moran

83 Shadow Play

Which of the shadows is that of the eagle shown here?

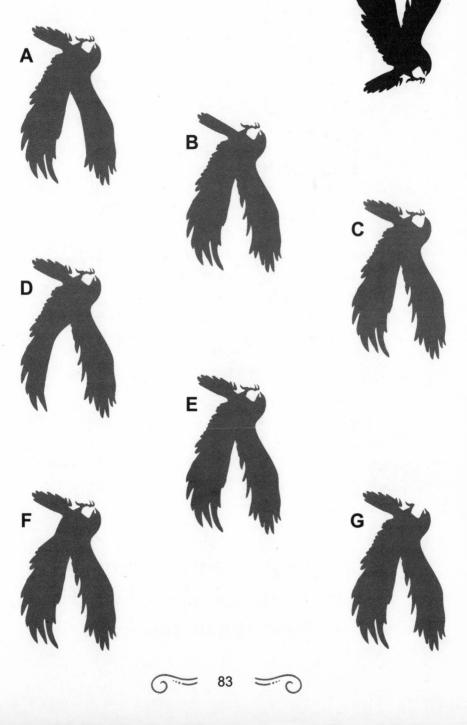

Wordsearch: Let's Go Camping

Can you find all of the listed camping words hidden in the grid below? Words run forward or backward, in either a horizontal, vertical or diagonal direction.

```
S Y H G W Q M M H E H K Q
U L A X J O A C I P E G S
S K E J O P T V K N A S C
J P P E S I Q Q I M K P C
W O O D P A V Q N V E L J
Z K S C K I E P G R S M L
S E P S K T N A U O A B G
Y T A Y E E E G H T Q I Q
S T O Z R N T L B I V E N
T L A P L E R K L A D P E
O E D L E E L E N I G A D
V M I J B S M T D I K C I
E R O P E S Z A U L F S U
G N I N W A R M R C I E G
F E E A N W Q C O F D W U
```

AWNING	KETTLE	ROPES
CUTLERY	MAPS	SKILLET
ESCAPE	PEGS	SLEEPING BAG
FRAME	PITCH	STOVE
GRILL	POCKET KNIFE	WILDERNESS
GUIDE	POTS	WOOD
HIKING	RAIN	

 "When you realize nothing is lacking, the whole world belongs to you."

Lao Tzu

Criss Cross: Too Much Noise!

The words are provided, but can you fit them all into the grid?

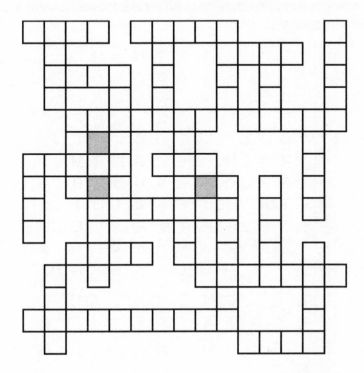

3 letters
RAP

4 letters
BARK
BRAY
ECHO
FIZZ
HISS
HONK
HOWL
SLAM
THUD

WAIL
WHAM
YELP

5 letters
BLAST
CHIME
CLANG
CLINK
KNOCK
SMACK
TWEET
WHINE

7 letters
CLATTER
PEALING
PINGING
SCRATCH
SCREECH
WHISTLE

10 letters
TRUMPETING

Wordsearch: Cheese Board

Can you find all of the listed cheeses hidden in the grid below?
Words run forward or backward, in either a horizontal, vertical or
diagonal direction.

```
D R Z R K G A F M X X B X
W C T P N J A T H V L R V
I A D Q P E L R T M R I C
G B U S U J D Y I O H E B
M O N T E R E Y J A C K M
O C L E F P B L E A K I X
R Z O D U R V X L L J F R
E N P S E F R I E S I A N
G I R D W Y C O T F I R E
R U Q O K I O H U B I Q I
U E B V C N S R A L Q R F
Y D L B T A T S K T E I O
E A S V E N N N V S E G Q
R M R A T E F A A E M L J
E C T G V O N K Y B U E E
```

ACORN	FETA	NEUFCHATEL
AIRAG	FRIESIAN	OLDE YORK
BRIE	GRUYERE	RICOTTA
CABOC	GUBBEEN	SWISS
DERBY	KASERI	WIGMORE
DUNLOP	LEYDEN	YARG
EDAM	MONTEREY JACK	

87   Letterboxes

Every row and column in the grid below originally contained one each of the letters A, B, C, D, E and F, with none appearing more than once in any row or column.

The letters outside the grid show which letter will appear first from that direction. Can you complete the grid?

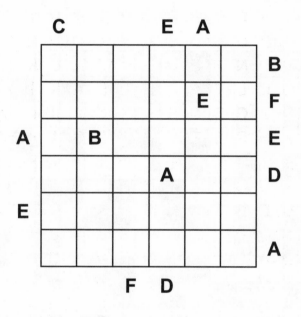

88   Odd One Out

Which number is the odd one out, and why is it different?

4123	8646
7355	3217
6488	9546
2189	7284

89   Codeword

Every letter in this puzzle has been replaced by a number, the number remaining the same for that letter wherever it occurs. Every letter of the alphabet has been used. Substitute numbers for letters to complete the codeword.

It may help to cross off the letters beneath the grid to keep a track of progress, and to use the reference box showing which numbers have been decoded. Three letters have already been entered into the grid, to help you on your way.

13		3		1		24	10	13	15	25	26	15	8	16
18	13	17	14	19		10			26		13		13	
4		22		19	15	3	14	3	17	13	25	19	15	22
22	18	26	8	8		5			19		26		14	
		9		19		5	8	19	2	26	15	4	19	25 T
4	19	25	13	14	26		19		17			15		19 O
13		3		3		3			12	8	26	26	4 P
22		23		22	4	13	25	25	26	15		11		4
25	15	19	10	25		26			26		10		8	
26		15		26		15		4	13	7	7	8	26	
22	9	26	17	25	8	26	22	22		20		3		
	21		13		13		13		5	19	9	13	8	
21	13	26	18	19	4	21	3	8	3	13		3		16
	3		26		22		25		22	4	13	2	17	
12	15	3	7	8	26	2	13	16		25		8		6

A B C D E F G H I J K L M
N O P Q R S T U V W X Y Z

1	2	3	4 P	5	6	7	8	9	10	11	12	13
14	15	16	17	18	19 O	20	21	22	23	24	25 T	26

90   Arroword

Solve the clues, then enter each answer in the direction of the arrows, one letter per square.

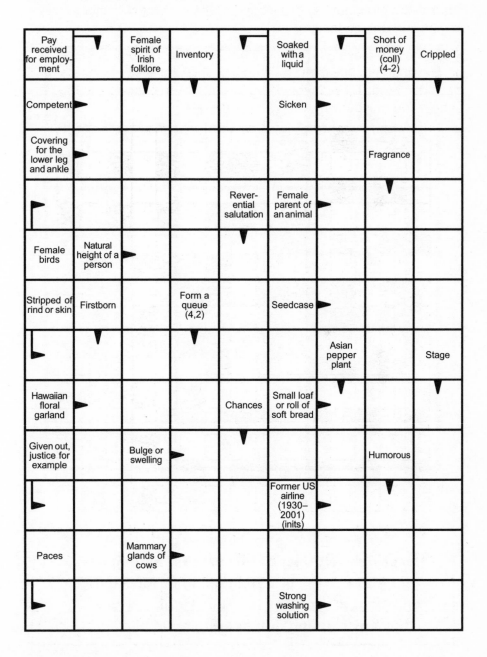

The grid clues:

- Pay received for employment
- Female spirit of Irish folklore
- Inventory
- Soaked with a liquid
- Short of money (coll) (4-2)
- Crippled
- Competent
- Sicken
- Covering for the lower leg and ankle
- Fragrance
- Reverential salutation
- Female parent of an animal
- Female birds
- Natural height of a person
- Stripped of rind or skin
- Firstborn
- Form a queue (4,2)
- Seedcase
- Asian pepper plant
- Stage
- Hawaiian floral garland
- Chances
- Small loaf or roll of soft bread
- Given out, justice for example
- Bulge or swelling
- Humorous
- Former US airline (1930–2001) (inits)
- Paces
- Mammary glands of cows
- Strong washing solution

Sudoku

Place one of the numbers from 1 to 9 into every empty cell so that each row, each column and each 3x3 block contains all the numbers from 1 to 9.

1		2		3		4		5
	4		5		8		9	
5				2				8
7		5	2		6	3		9
	2		9		3		5	
8		9	1		5	2		6
3				9				7
	7		8		2		1	
2		1		6		9		4

"There's only one reason why you're not experiencing bliss at this present moment, and it's because you're thinking or focusing on what you don't have.... But, right now you have everything you need to be in bliss."

Anthony de Mello

92   Shape Up

Every row and column in this grid originally contained one circle, one diamond, one square, one triangle and two blank squares, although not necessarily in that order.

Every symbol with a black arrow refers to the first of the four symbols encountered when travelling in the direction of the arrow. Every symbol with a white arrow refers to the second of the four symbols encountered in the direction of the arrow.

Can you complete the original grid?

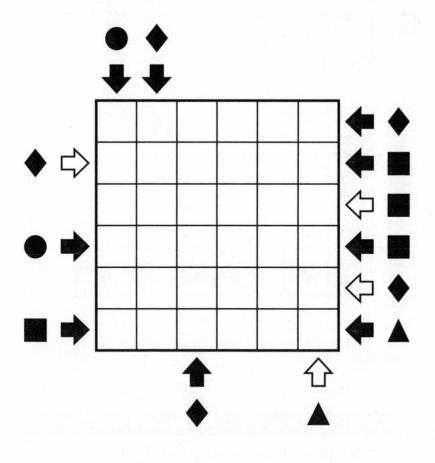

93   Domino Placement

A standard set of twenty-eight dominoes has been laid out as shown below. Can you draw in the edges of them all?

It may be helpful to use the check-box to tick off the dominoes as they are found.

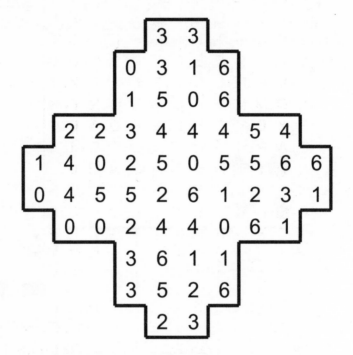

0-0	0-1	0-2	0-3	0-4	0-5	0-6	1-1

1-2	1-3	1-4	1-5	1-6	2-2	2-3	2-4	2-5	2-6

3-3	3-4	3-5	3-6	4-4	4-5	4-6	5-5	5-6	6-6

94   Wordsearch: Three "E"s

Can you find all of the listed words containing three Es hidden in the grid below? Words run forward or backward, in either a horizontal, vertical or diagonal direction.

E	A	Z	T	Z	F	R	E	M	M	Y	T	R
R	X	L	K	R	G	E	E	S	E	S	E	H
E	B	C	S	T	L	F	Q	D	E	D	C	C
S	L	X	E	E	E	D	Y	R	E	T	U	U
T	V	E	M	L	D	U	E	E	A	E	Z	T
L	Q	M	M	V	L	D	M	B	D	N	F	N
E	X	E	V	E	N	E	E	R	O	A	E	G
S	A	R	B	E	N	I	N	O	P	C	J	E
S	D	T	T	Q	E	T	N	T	N	M	L	E
N	R	X	L	S	T	L	A	E	X	Q	E	N
E	M	E	R	G	E	A	T	E	T	R	C	R
S	C	X	H	F	H	N	I	E	G	E	E	E
S	T	J	M	H	E	R	J	E	E	Q	E	T
J	E	E	S	S	E	R	D	D	A	B	L	N
R	E	T	T	E	S	D	N	E	R	T	F	I

ADDRESSEE	EXTREME	REDEEM
BEETLE	FEEDER	RESTLESSNESS
DEGREE	FLEECE	SENTENCE
EERIE	GEESE	TENDEREST
ELEMENT	INTERNEE	TRENDSETTER
EMERGE	MELEE	VENEER
EXCELLENT	NINETEEN	

"The real meditation is how you live your life."

Jon Kabat-Zinn

Criss Cross: Operas

The words are provided, but can you fit them all into the grid?

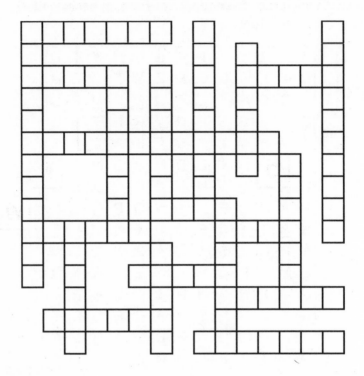

4 letters
AIDA
LULU

5 letters
MEDEE
NORMA
SERSE
THAIS

6 letters
ALCINA
CARMEN

OTELLO
SALOME
SEMELE

7 letters
ALCESTE
MACBETH
NABUCCO
RUSALKA
WERTHER

8 letters
AKHNATEN

9 letters
BILLY BUDD

10 letters
LES TROYENS

12 letters
LA
  SONNAMBULA
MANON
  LESCAUT

96   Mind Over Matter

Given that the letters are valued 1-26 according to their places in the alphabet, can you crack the code to reveal the missing letter?

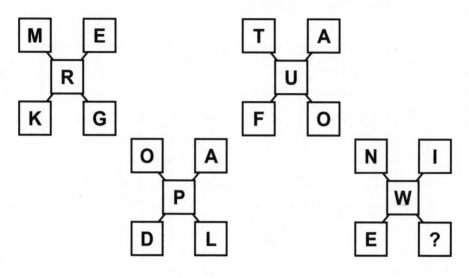

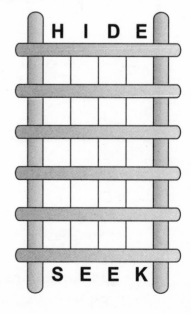

97   Word Ladder

Change one letter at a time (but not the position of any letter) to make a new word – and move from the word at the top of the ladder to the word at the bottom using the exact number of rungs provided.

HIDE

SEEK

Sudoku

Place one of the numbers from 1 to 9 into every empty cell so that each row, each column and each 3x3 block contains all the numbers from 1 to 9.

		2	4			7	5	
	3		2		8	1		
	4	9	1	3				
7			3	9				2
9		3				5		6
1				2	5			9
				7	2	9	3	
		8	5		6		4	
	7	5			3	8		

"Success is peace of mind which is a
direct result of self-satisfaction in knowing
you did your best to become the best
you are capable of becoming."

John Wooden

Broken Tiles

Four tiles have each been broken into three pieces. Can you match the pieces of every tile? Any piece may be rotated.

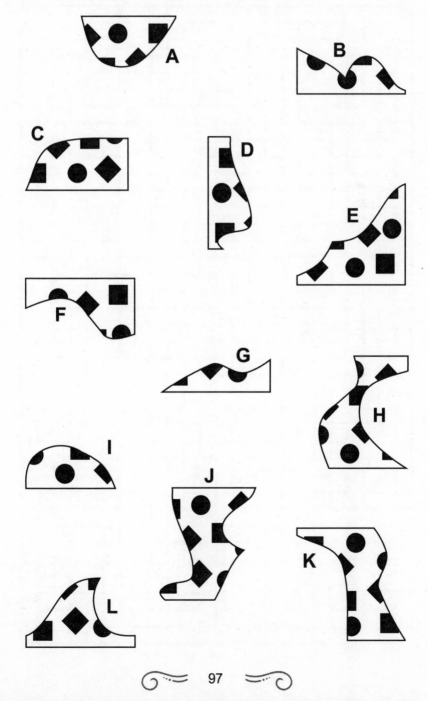

100   Maze

Find a path from one circle to the other through this maze.

101   Codeword

Every letter in this puzzle has been replaced by a number, the number remaining the same for that letter wherever it occurs. Every letter of the alphabet has been used. Substitute numbers for letters to complete the codeword.

It may help to cross off the letters beneath the grid to keep a track of progress, and to use the reference box showing which numbers have been decoded. Three letters have already been entered into the grid, to help you on your way.

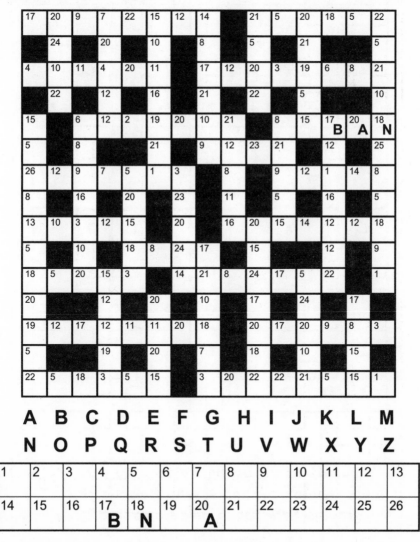

A B C D E F G H I J K L M
N O P Q R S T U V W X Y Z

1	2	3	4	5	6	7	8	9	10	11	12	13
14	15	16	17 **B**	18 **N**	19	20 **A**	21	22	23	24	25	26

Tic-Tac-Toe

Place either O or X into each empty square, so that no four consecutive squares in a straight line in any direction (horizontally, vertically, or diagonally) contain more than three of the same symbol.

O	X		X	X			O	X
O		X		X				X
		X				X		O
		O	X		O		O	O
O	X			X		X		X
X	X		X					
		O		X		X		X
X		X				O	O	
O	X			O			X	
	O			O	O			O
O		O	X	O	X		X	
O	O	O			X	O		

"Your vision will become clear only when you look into your heart. Who looks outside, dreams. Who looks inside, awakens."

Carl Jung

103   **Sudoku**

Place one of the numbers from 1 to 9 into every empty cell so that each row, each column and each 3x3 block contains all the numbers from 1 to 9.

6	2			1		5	9	
			8	6	7			
3		1					8	
7	3	2	1			9		
1			6		2			8
		5			9	4	1	2
	9					3		1
			2	4	6			
	8	7		9			5	6

"Our own worst enemy cannot harm us as much as our unwise thoughts. No one can help us as much as our own compassionate thoughts."

Buddha

104   Wordsearch: Archery

Can you find all of the listed archery words hidden in the grid below?
Words run forward or backward, in either a horizontal, vertical or
diagonal direction.

S	T	C	N	B	V	D	T	E	G	R	A	T
F	S	I	G	H	T	T	Z	N	F	Y	F	I
A	E	W	E	Y	N	Z	I	U	N	A	P	L
S	R	L	X	P	O	K	J	U	H	D	F	H
T	W	M	A	H	C	S	A	S	I	Y	Y	F
U	O	X	T	A	K	I	L	H	O	R	L	Q
P	R	R	T	W	M	Q	X	O	M	E	L	O
P	R	S	Q	I	U	G	V	T	T	R	E	H
E	A	A	N	U	N	U	Z	C	E	G	B	O
R	G	G	K	A	E	K	H	D	A	Y	C	L
L	Z	L	M	V	I	E	R	D	C	P	J	D
I	B	W	H	P	R	I	N	Y	T	I	U	B
M	O	T	H	T	N	U	T	E	T	A	L	P
B	E	O	C	G	O	P	A	G	Q	X	Q	A
Z	D	C	W	P	E	Q	A	E	G	P	O	V

AIMING	HOLD	SIGHT
ARROW REST	NOCK	STACKING
ASCHAM	PLATE	TARGET
BELLY	POUNDAGE	TORQUE
BOWMAN	RED RING	UPPER LIMB
FAST	SHAFT	YEW
FLETCHER	SHOT	

"Be happy in the moment,
that's enough. Each moment
is all we need, not more."

Mother Teresa

Arroword

Solve the clues, then enter each answer in the direction of the arrows, one letter per square.

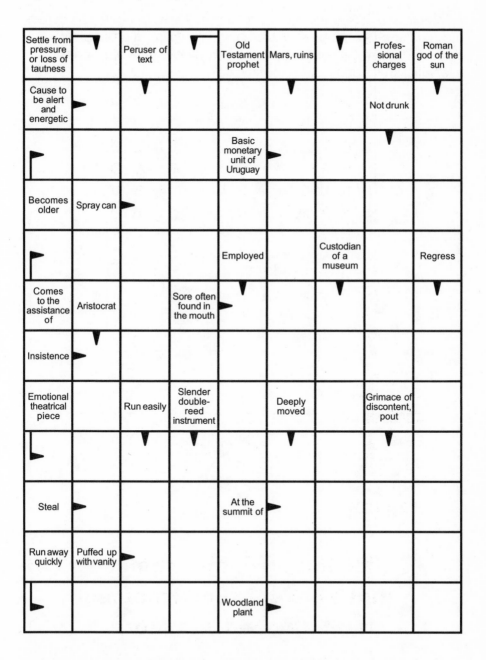

106   Buy Buy

Seven coffee-pots were displayed as you see them in the top picture, before Mrs Jones came into the shop and bought one.

However, she picked them all up to look at them very carefully before making her choice, then replaced them in a different order after inspecting them, so we aren't sure exactly which one Mrs Jones eventually purchased. Can you decide?

Before

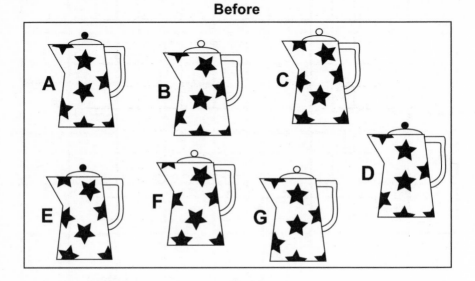

After

107   Criss Cross: Brave Words

The words are provided, but can you fit them all into the grid?

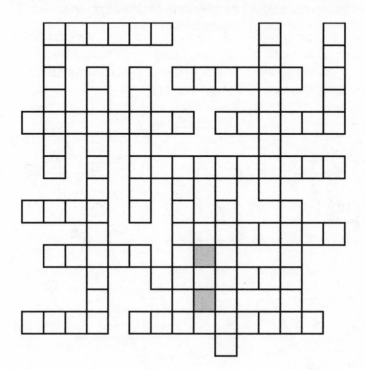

4 letters
BOLD
GAME

5 letters
HARDY
MANLY

6 letters
FEISTY
GRITTY
HEROIC
METTLE

7 letters
GALLANT
STOICAL
VALIANT

8 letters
FEARLESS
SPIRITED
UNAFRAID
VALOROUS

9 letters
AUDACIOUS
UNDAUNTED

10 letters
COURAGEOUS

12 letters
STOUT-HEARTED

Hexagony

Can you place the hexagons into the grid, so that where any hexagon touches another along a straight line, the contents of both triangles is the same? No rotation of any hexagon is allowed!

109   Codeword

Every letter in this puzzle has been replaced by a number, the number remaining the same for that letter wherever it occurs. Every letter of the alphabet has been used. Substitute numbers for letters to complete the codeword.

It may help to cross off the letters beneath the grid to keep a track of progress, and to use the reference box showing which numbers have been decoded. Three letters have already been entered into the grid, to help you on your way.

1	17	15	6	6	15	21	25	11		24	15	22	18	24
17		11		18		23		23		26		18		18
23	13	11	15	7		10	23	21	5	15	8	14		9
2		17		16		12		5		22		25		23
18	9	9	25	3	15	9	2		22	18	26	8	25	11
		15		26			9		19				25
23	12	23	18		21	23	10	7	11	25	21	18	8	2
12		8		4		8		17		3		14		18
20	17	9	2	15	4	3	15	8	14		21	23	11	24
18			11		13				21		2			
21 **C**	23 **O**	11 **L**	17	10	8		21	11	23	17	24	15	18	26
2		25		14		21		25		21		9		15
23		8	23	23	24	11	18	9		5	15	2	18	9
26		21		18		15		9		23		15		18
9	16	18	18	26		7	26	23	12	23	9	21	15	9

A B C D E F G H I J K L M
N O P Q R S T U V W X Y Z

1	2	3	4	5	6	7	8	9	10	11 **L**	12	13
14	15	16	17	18	19	20	21 **C**	22	23 **O**	24	25	26

Total Concentration

The blank squares below should be filled with whole numbers between 1 and 40 inclusive, any of which may occur more than once, or not at all.

The numbers in every horizontal row add up to the totals on the right, as do the two long diagonal lines; whilst those in every vertical column add up to the totals along the bottom.

Can you discover the missing numbers?

								136
22	4	9			26		32	155
37		36	19		18	30	1	189
28	28	37	28	10		10	18	168
11	26		40		7		18	163
	9	20	3	1	18	2	24	110
25	12		8	36	15	1	39	141
		13		35	30	1		138
32	38		13	31		34	22	206
207	145	139	125	194	153	124	183	159

Sudoku

Place one of the numbers from 1 to 9 into every empty cell so that
each row, each column and each 3x3 block contains all the numbers
from 1 to 9.

	1		5				6	8
5	7	2			4			
3			7	9		5		
	5			4		8		7
	2		1		9		3	
4		9		5			2	
		7		1	2			9
			6			3	8	4
6	4				8		7	

"Doubt is an uneasy and dissatisfied state from
which we struggle to free ourselves and pass
into the state of belief; while the latter is a calm
and satisfactory state which we do not wish to
avoid, or to change to a belief in anything else."

Charles Sanders Peirce

112   Word Wheel

How many words of three or more letters can you make from those in the wheel, without using plurals, abbreviations or proper nouns?

The central letter must appear once in every word and no letter in a section of the wheel may be used more than once.

There is at least one nine-letter word in the wheel.

Nine-letter word(s):

_____

113   Zigzag

The object of this puzzle is to trace a single path from the top left corner to the bottom right corner of the grid, moving through all of the cells (tracking through the numbers in the sequence 1-2-3-4-5-6-7-8-1-2-3-4-5-6-7-8, etc) in either a horizontal, vertical or diagonal direction.

1	5	6	1	2	4	5	6
2	3	4	7	8	3	8	7
6	5	4	2	1	4	2	1
7	1	3	7	8	3	5	6
8	2	3	5	6	5	7	8
2	1	4	6	4	3	2	1
3	8	7	7	1	3	6	7
4	5	6	8	2	4	5	8

Wordsearch: Canals

Can you find all of the listed canals hidden in the grid below? Words run forward or backward, in either a horizontal, vertical or diagonal direction.

```
E L A D H C O R S U E Z E
R D F P V C F A X F A N N
P O R S Q R M I A M I O K
P E A K F O R E S T I E S
I F N L U Y K R S T N A N
O H K E J D U Z C N D S H
N A L I F O I N E R T H X
E V I K N N U T R E N T O
E E N Q B J A Y A G V O G
R L R R D N D U P E N N E
B L I N D O G Y V N M U W
V T A A B U I R N T Y S S
Z R V L S S S A G S U A O
G O O T U B M O R R I S J
N X A R T V J C R K X Y W
```

ASHTON	KENNET AND AVON	PIONEER
AUGUSTA		REGENT'S
BRITZ	KIEL	ROCHDALE
CROYDON	LINDO	STINE
FRANKLIN	MIAMI	SUEZ
GRAND JUNCTION	MORRIS	TRENT
	OSWEGO	
HAVEL	PEAK FOREST	

"Mindfulness isn't difficult, we just need to remember to do it."

Sharon Salzberg

Sudoku

Place one of the numbers from 1 to 9 into every empty cell so that each row, each column and each 3x3 block contains all the numbers from 1 to 9.

3				4			7	
	2		8		9	3		
	9	5	6		1	2		
		7	2				9	6
		8		1		5		
5	4				3	1		
		4	1		6	8	3	
		3	7		5		6	
	5			8				2

"Learn to enjoy every minute of your life. Be happy now. Don't wait for something outside of yourself to make you happy in the future. Think how really precious is the time you have to spend, whether it's at work or with your family. Every minute should be enjoyed and savored."

Earl Nightingale

The words are provided, but can you fit them all into the grid?

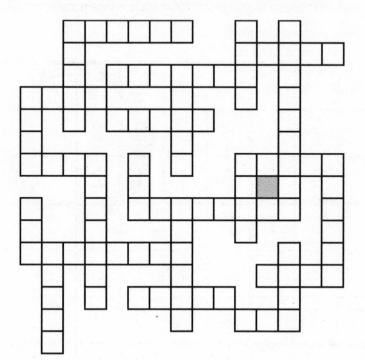

3 letters
CUB
FRY
KID

4 letters
CALF
COLT
CRIA
FAWN
FOAL
JOEY
LAMB

5 letters
CHICK
ELVER
NYMPH
OWLET
POULT
PUPPY
WHELP

6 letters
CYGNET
KITTEN
PIGLET

7 letters
LEVERET
TADPOLE

8 letters
DUCKLING
YEARLING

9 letters
FLEDGLING

117 Word Wheel

How many words of three or more letters can you make from those in the wheel, without using plurals, abbreviations or proper nouns?

The central letter must appear once in every word and no letter in a section of the wheel may be used more than once.

There is at least one nine-letter word in the wheel.

Nine-letter word(s):

_____

118 Word Ladder

Change one letter at a time (but not the position of any letter) to make a new word – and move from the word at the top of the ladder to the word at the bottom using the exact number of rungs provided.

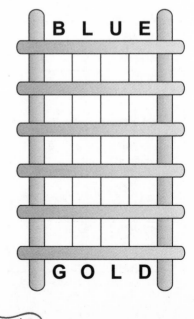

Arroword

Solve the clues, then enter each answer in the direction of the arrows, one letter per square.

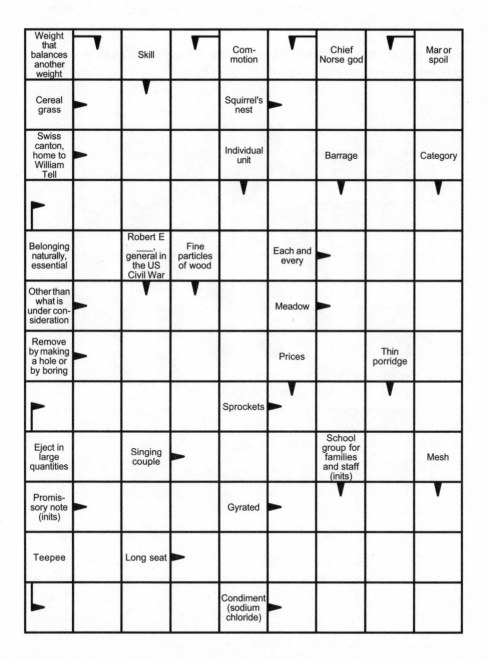

The grid contains the following clues:

- Weight that balances another weight
- Skill
- Commotion
- Chief Norse god
- Mar or spoil
- Cereal grass
- Squirrel's nest
- Swiss canton, home to William Tell
- Individual unit
- Barrage
- Category
- Belonging naturally, essential
- Robert E ___, general in the US Civil War
- Fine particles of wood
- Each and every
- Other than what is under consideration
- Meadow
- Remove by making a hole or by boring
- Prices
- Thin porridge
- Sprockets
- Eject in large quantities
- Singing couple
- School group for families and staff (inits)
- Mesh
- Promissory note (inits)
- Gyrated
- Teepee
- Long seat
- Condiment (sodium chloride)

120   Codeword

Every letter in this puzzle has been replaced by a number, the number remaining the same for that letter wherever it occurs. Every letter of the alphabet has been used. Substitute numbers for letters to complete the codeword.

It may help to cross off the letters beneath the grid to keep a track of progress, and to use the reference box showing which numbers have been decoded. Three letters have already been entered into the grid, to help you on your way.

25	15	2	20	7	22			15	23	24 T	17 O	13 N	11	23	16
21		22		17				5		10		24			11
6	17	7	7	21	23	9		21		22	14	15	7	24	
12		11		23		17	13	11	17	13		7			16
2	17	9	1	4		15		2		23	16	11	13	22	
17			2		26	7	17	24	4			9		2	
18	22	12	15	7	17		19		22	15	24	23			
23			11		13	11	13	8	15		11			2	
		23	24	4	22		22			2	22	13	22	25	22
13		16			23	22	12	15	13		22			10	
17	18	22	2	15		13		10		6	15	21	10	22	
6		2		3	17	2	25	22		15		13		2	
15	7	11	20	11		15		2	22	8	17	11	13	23	
12		3		2		25				17		24		22	
23	21	3	3	22	2	22	12		20	2	15	4	22	12	

A B C D E F G H I J K L M
N O P Q R S T U V W X Y Z

1	2	3	4	5	6	7	8	9	10	11	12	13 N
14	15	16	17 O	18	19	20	21	22	23	24 T	25	26

121 Sudoku

Place one of the numbers from 1 to 9 into every empty cell so that each row, each column and each 3x3 block contains all the numbers from 1 to 9.

	3		5			7		8
	5			6	7	2	9	
2			1			6		
		3		9			7	2
9			7		5			1
6	4			1		5		
		8			4			7
	2	4	6	8			3	
1		5			2		4	

"The way to live in the present is to remember that 'This too shall pass.' When you experience joy, remembering that 'This too shall pass' helps you savor the here and now. When you experience pain and sorrow, remembering that 'This too shall pass' reminds you that grief, like joy, is only temporary."

Joey Green

Eliminator

Every oval shape contains a different letter of the alphabet from A to K inclusive. Use the clues to determine their locations. Reference in the clues to 'due' means in any location along the same horizontal or vertical line.

1 The A is due east of both the C and the J.

2 The B is due east of the I, due west of the H and due north of the G.

3 The C is next to and south of the K, which is next to and west of the D.

4 The E is further south and further east than the F, which is next to the D.

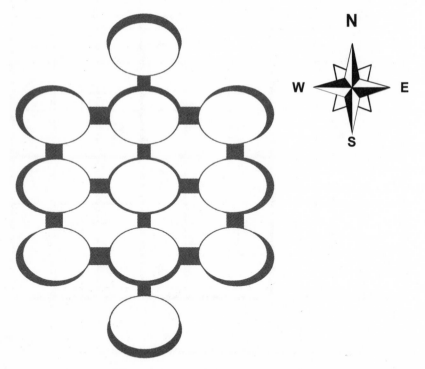

"The most precious gift we can offer others is our presence. When mindfulness embraces those we love, they will bloom like flowers."

Thich Nhat Hanh

123   Coin Collecting

In this puzzle, an amateur coin collector has been out with his metal detector, searching for booty. He didn't have time to dig up all the coins he found, so has made a grid map, showing their locations, in the hope that if he loses the map, at least no-one else will understand it…

Those squares containing numbers are empty, but where a number appears in a square, it indicates how many coins are located in the squares (up to a maximum of eight) surrounding the numbered one, touching it at any corner or side. There is only one coin in any individual square.

Place a circle into every square containing a coin.

	2			0		0		2	
2				2	1		2		
					2			3	
0		2							2
		1		2		1	3		
							3	4	3
	2	1			2				
			0			3	3		
0						3	3		2
			2				2		

"Do not dwell in the past, do not dream of the future, concentrate the mind on the present moment."

Buddha

Wordsearch: Wales

Can you find all of the listed Welsh place names hidden in the grid below? Words run forward or backward, in either a horizontal, vertical or diagonal direction.

E	E	C	T	Y	I	N	C	O	N	W	Y	V
A	G	R	F	Y	L	C	X	S	U	B	T	O
F	H	S	T	Y	P	L	W	M	P	U	A	H
R	U	X	H	N	A	N	T	M	D	C	G	G
O	G	R	N	E	E	N	R	D	B	I	P	T
M	W	E	D	F	I	P	D	R	B	R	N	O
H	B	K	Y	L	J	Y	E	N	E	E	A	S
O	D	N	F	I	H	L	E	S	A	I	N	N
E	L	Y	P	R	E	D	T	T	E	K	T	O
G	D	F	W	G	H	A	H	M	S	N	L	L
T	C	Z	N	W	T	Y	F	V	N	B	L	P
C	E	A	G	Y	C	L	D	R	A	E	E	G
B	L	N	N	S	R	Q	X	D	W	A	I	K
L	E	B	B	W	V	A	L	E	S	K	W	W
I	O	Y	N	Y	S	L	A	S	T	Q	F	S

CONWY	NANTLLE	PYLE
CWMBRAN	NEATH	RHYD DDU
DENBIGH	NEBO	RHYL
EBBW VALE	NEFYN	SWANSEA
FLINT	PENTRE	TENBY
LLANGELER	PLWMP	YNYSLAS
MORFA	PRESTATYN	

"If you want to conquer the anxiety of life, live in the moment, live in the breath."

Amit Ray

125   Criss Cross: All Together

The words are provided, but can you fit them all into the grid?

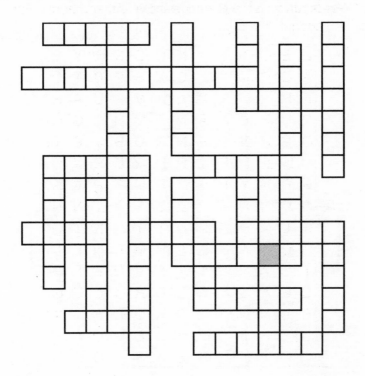

4 letters	5 letters	7 letters
BAND	BUNCH	CLUSTER
CLUB	CLUMP	COMPANY
GANG	CROWD	
HEAP	FLOCK	8 letters
HERD	GROUP	ASSEMBLE
MASS	PARTY	
PACK	SHEAF	9 letters
PILE	SWARM	MULTITUDE
TEAM		
TUFT	6 letters	11 letters
	BUNDLE	CONJUNCTION
	GATHER	
	STRING	

126   Domino Placement

A standard set of twenty-eight dominoes has been laid out as shown below. Can you draw in the edges of them all?

It may be helpful to use the check-box to tick off the dominoes as they are found.

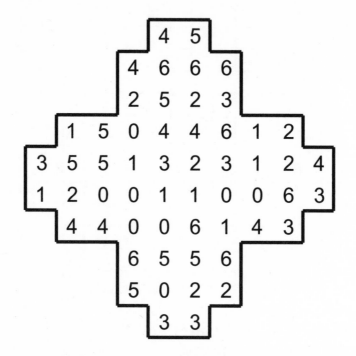

0-0	0-1	0-2	0-3	0-4	0-5	0-6	1-1

1-2	1-3	1-4	1-5	1-6	2-2	2-3	2-4	2-5	2-6

3-3	3-4	3-5	3-6	4-4	4-5	4-6	5-5	5-6	6-6

127 **Round Up**

The number in each circle is the sum of the two numbers below it.
Just work out the missing numbers in every circle!

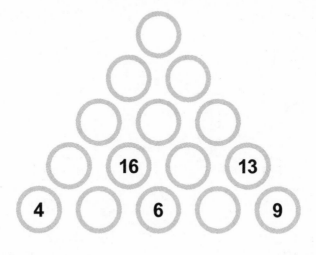

128 **Calculate**

What letter should replace the question mark in the final calculation?

$$R \div I = B$$

$$B + J = L$$

$$P - E = K$$

$$G \times C = ?$$

Number Cruncher

Starting at the top left with the number provided, work down from one box to another, applying the mathematical instructions to your running total.

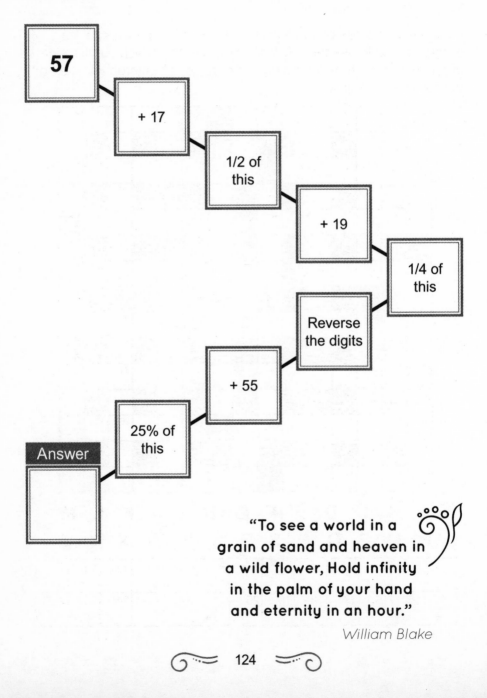

57

+ 17

1/2 of this

+ 19

1/4 of this

Reverse the digits

+ 55

25% of this

Answer

"To see a world in a grain of sand and heaven in a wild flower, Hold infinity in the palm of your hand and eternity in an hour."

William Blake

130   Codeword

Every letter in this puzzle has been replaced by a number, the number remaining the same for that letter wherever it occurs. Every letter of the alphabet has been used. Substitute numbers for letters to complete the codeword.

It may help to cross off the letters beneath the grid to keep a track of progress, and to use the reference box showing which numbers have been decoded. Three letters have already been entered into the grid, to help you on your way.

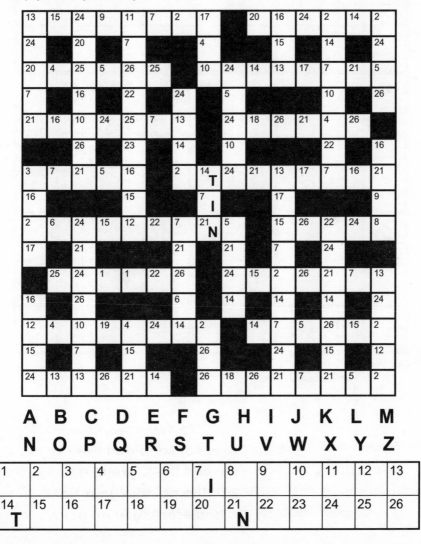

A	B	C	D	E	F	G	H	I	J	K	L	M
N	O	P	Q	R	S	T	U	V	W	X	Y	Z

1	2	3	4	5	6	7 I	8	9	10	11	12	13
14 T	15	16	17	18	19	20	21 N	22	23	24	25	26

Sudoku

Place one of the numbers from 1 to 9 into every empty cell so that each row, each column and each 3x3 block contains all the numbers from 1 to 9.

	5		6				1	9	
4	2	6			8				
		3	2	7				6	
7		8		6			4		
	4		5		7		3		
	6			8		2		1	
2				5	4	7			
			9			8	1	3	
	8	9			1		2		

"Mindfulness means being aware of how you're deploying your attention and making decisions about it, and not letting the tweet or the buzzing of your BlackBerry call your attention."

Howard Rheingold

132   Arroword

Solve the clues, then enter each answer in the direction of the arrows, one letter per square.

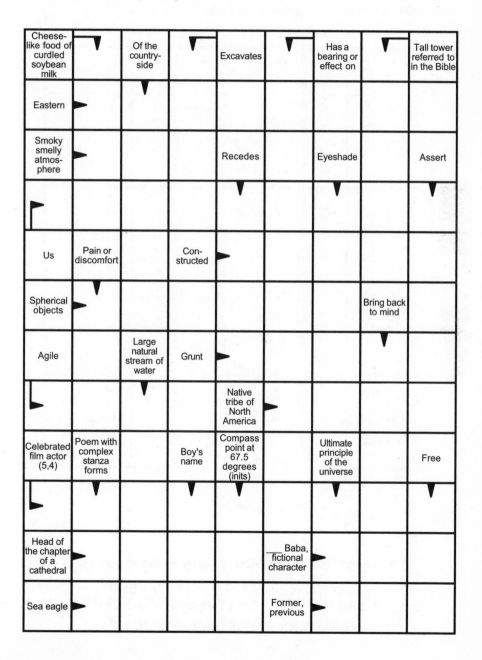

133   Wordsearch: Islands

Can you find all of the listed islands of the southern seas hidden in the grid below? Words run forward or backward, in either a horizontal, vertical or diagonal direction.

```
R C C D I J B S P V V T X
R T Z A A A Y P R A X L E
P N V A N U A L E V U R Y
K R S A M T A S R C E U C
I I B P L N O R T T P H F
R A S K A H M N S I M S I
I C C I H M N A C H M N J
B T S P A A E U U V N O I
A I N R W F W T A G A H R
T P E L U K L A I B E O T
I S Z O F N R U I C T E F
K A N D A V U N B I A N V
A O R U R U M A E O I R W
K P R M J A R V I S A O I
U U A E E C F W N M R B B
```

BANABA   HONSHU   PITCAIRN

BORNEO   JARVIS   RAIATEA

CANTON   KANDAVU   SERAM

EASTER   KIRIBATI   TIMOR

FIJI   LANAI   VANUA LEVU

GUAM   MURUROA   VANUATU

HAWAII   NAURU

"Each morning we are born again. What we do today is what matters most."

Buddha

　　　Criss Cross: Palindromes

The words are provided, but can you fit them all into the grid?

3 letters
DAD
DID
EWE

4 letters
ANNA
DEED
KOOK
NOON
OTTO
PEEP
SEES

5 letters
CIVIC
KAYAK
LEVEL
PUT UP
RADAR
REFER
ROTOR
SAGAS
SEXES
SHAHS
SOLOS
STATS
TENET

6 letters
HANNAH
REDDER

7 letters
DEIFIED
RACE-CAR
REPAPER
REVIVER
ROTATOR

135   Sudoku

Place one of the numbers from 1 to 9 into every empty cell so that each row, each column and each 3x3 block contains all the numbers from 1 to 9.

	4			9	8		7	
3					5			9
2	9	5				3	8	6
6					4		5	
		2	7		3	6		
	1		9					8
7	6	3				8	2	1
4			8					7
	5		2	1			6	

"You practice mindfulness, on the one hand, to be calm and peaceful. On the other hand, as you practice mindfulness and live a life of peace, you inspire hope for a future of peace."

Thich Nhat Hanh

136 Codeword

Every letter in this puzzle has been replaced by a number, the number remaining the same for that letter wherever it occurs. Every letter of the alphabet has been used. Substitute numbers for letters to complete the codeword.

It may help to cross off the letters beneath the grid to keep a track of progress, and to use the reference box showing which numbers have been decoded. Three letters have already been entered into the grid, to help you on your way.

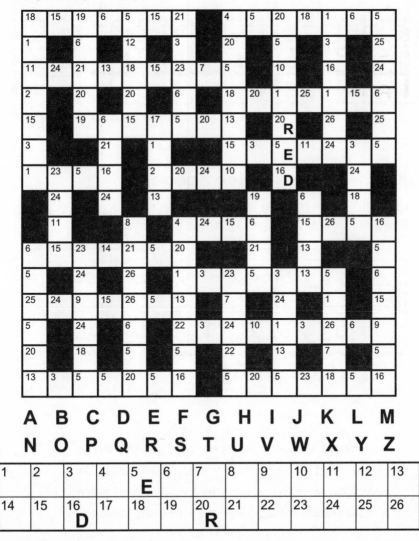

18	15	19	6	5	15	21		4	5	20	18	1	6	5
1		6		12		3		20		5		3		25
11	24	21	13	18	15	23	7	5		10		16		24
2		20		20		6		18	20	1	25	1	15	6
15		19	6	15	17	5	20	13		20 **R**		26		25
3			21		1			15	3	5 **E**	11	24	3	5
1	23	5	16		2	20	24	10		16 **D**			24	
	24		24		13			19		6		18		
	11			8		4	24	15	6		15	26	5	16
6	15	23	14	21	5	20			21		13			5
5		24		26		1	3	23	5	3	13	5		6
25	24	9	15	26	5	13		7		24		1		15
5		24		6		22	3	24	10	1	3	26	6	9
20		18		5		5		22		13		7		5
13	3	5	5	20	5	16		5	20	5	23	18	5	16

A B C D E F G H I J K L M

N O P Q R S T U V W X Y Z

1	2	3	4	5 **E**	6	7	8	9	10	11	12	13
14	15	16 **D**	17	18	19	20 **R**	21	22	23	24	25	26

Whatever Next?

Which of the four lettered alternatives (A, B, C or D) fits most logically into the empty square?

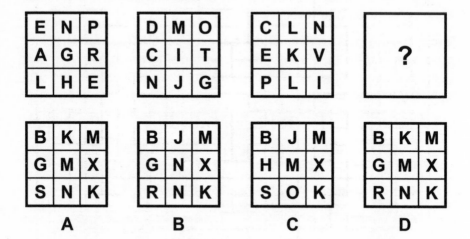

138

Shape Spotter

Which is the only shape to appear twice in the box below? You'll need a keen eye for this one, as some shapes overlap others!

139   Maze

Find a path from one circle to the other through this maze.

140   Sudoku

Place one of the numbers from 1 to 9 into every empty cell so that each row, each column and each 3x3 block contains all the numbers from 1 to 9.

1			8	3		7		
7	8	2			4			
	9		7				6	5
4		3		7			2	
	2		9		3		1	
	7			4		5		8
6	4				5		8	
			6			1	5	4
		8		9	2			3

"I'm a praying atheist. When I hear an ambulance siren, I ask for a blessing for those people in trouble, knowing that no one's listening. I think it's just a habit of mindfulness."

Geraldine Brooks

Hexagony

Can you place the hexagons into the grid, so that where any hexagon touches another along a straight line, the contents of both triangles is the same? No rotation of any hexagon is allowed!

142   Total Concentration

The blank squares below should be filled with whole numbers between 1 and 40 inclusive, any of which may occur more than once, or not at all.

The numbers in every horizontal row add up to the totals on the right, as do the two long diagonal lines; whilst those in every vertical column add up to the totals along the bottom.

Can you discover the missing numbers?

								127
5	32	26			6	24	14	152
13	30	25		29			13	182
	9	31	2	31	31	11		147
29	9		2	17		22	22	145
24			9		30	24	2	147
		15	1	25	39	35	30	175
21	3	33	38	17	16	37		173
14	25	29		32	13		26	188
124	150	177	141	193	180	204	140	203

143   Wordsearch: *Lord of the Rings*

Can you find all of the listed words hidden in the grid below? Words run forward or backward, in either a horizontal, vertical or diagonal direction.

```
F E A O C R L W L Z X B O
G O L I F I I N I Y K U G
N Q Y D X N K M A T K T B
G R R T N Q E O O H J T L
E D J I I I M O L R O E L
N Q E L V B W O W O O R O
R E M E M E B Y A J J B R
O I K T U E N O H I N U T
G B P O L M W D H T R R M
N A E I L N E R E G I O N
A L A O O E L R R L W W M
F R R R G W P D R D L T C
O O Z C A R M A K Y J M X
L G A S G A L O G A E M S
P P F E A S I I U X A I H
```

ARWEN	FANGORN	ORCS
BALROG	GIMLI	RIVENDELL
BOROMIR	GOLLUM	ROHAN
BUTTERBUR	HOBBIT	SMEAGOL
ELF	LOBELIA	TROLL
EOWYN	MERRY	WITHYWINDLE
EREGION	MORIA	

"Do every act of your life as though it were the last act of your life."

Marcus Aurelius

Odd One Out

One of these is different to the others in some way. Can you discover which is the odd one out, and say why?

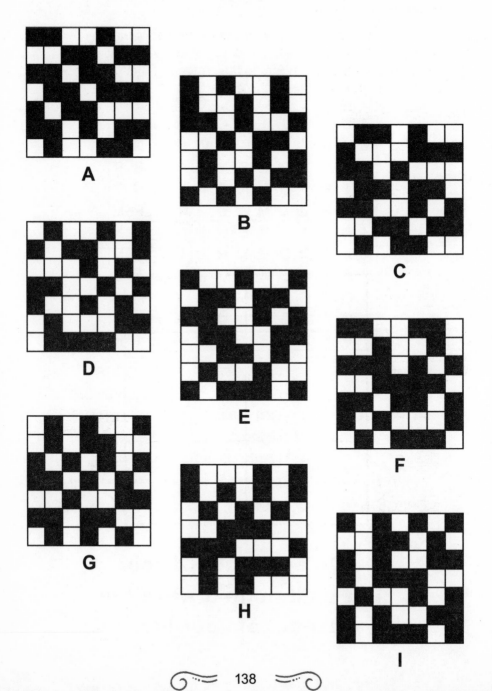

A

B

C

D

E

F

G

H

I

145   Shape Up

Every row and column in this grid originally contained one circle, one diamond, one square, one triangle and two blank squares, although not necessarily in that order.

Every symbol with a black arrow refers to the first of the four symbols encountered when travelling in the direction of the arrow. Every symbol with a white arrow refers to the second of the four symbols encountered in the direction of the arrow.

Can you complete the original grid?

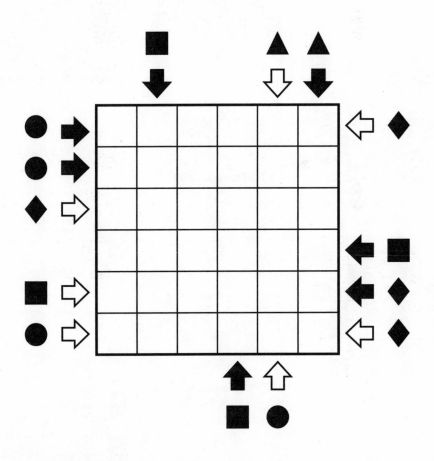

Mind Over Matter

Given that the letters are valued 1-26 according to their places in the alphabet, can you crack the code to reveal the missing letter?

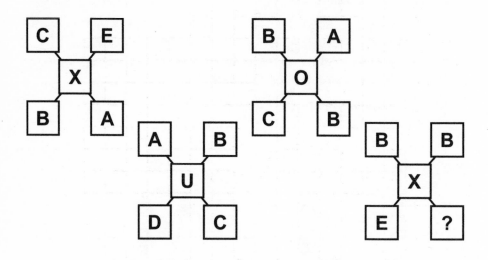

Word Ladder

Change one letter at a time (but not the position of any letter) to make a new word – and move from the word at the top of the ladder to the word at the bottom using the exact number of rungs provided.

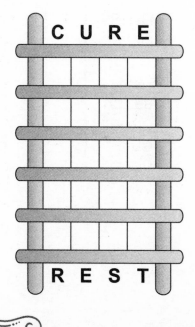

148   Criss Cross: On Vacation

The words are provided, but can you fit them all into the grid?

4 letters
MAPS

5 letters
BEACH
GROUP
GUIDE
HOTEL
VIEWS

6 letters
CAMERA
OUTING
VOYAGE

7 letters
AIRPORT
CAMPING
LUGGAGE
SCENERY
WALKING

8 letters
DUTY-FREE
POSTCARD

9 letters
EMBARKING

11 letters
TRAVEL AGENT

12 letters
TOUR
  OPERATOR

149 Arroword

Solve the clues, then enter each answer in the direction of the arrows, one letter per square.

Too	▾	Paved surface where aircraft stand	Make the sound of a dove	▾	Painting, sculpture, music, etc	Clean with hard rubbing	Native American tents, usually conical	▾
Ball game played with long-handled racquets ▸		▾	▾			▾		
Location ▸					Group of words		Groom	
▸				▾		▾		
Zodiacal prediction	Disen-tangle		Inanely foolish	Bait ▸				
Suddenly and unex-pectedly ▸	▾		▾					
French crescent-shaped roll		Exposed		Sun-related		Biblical character		Japanese short sword or dagger
⌐		▾		▾		▾		▾
Temporary cessation of breathing in sleep ▸							Abbrevia-tion for a particular month of the year	
Garment that covers the head and face ▸					Directed or controlled ▸		▾	
▸					Known ▸			
Red dye	Plant, commonly known as sea holly ▸							

Tic-Tac-Toe

Place either O or X into each empty square, so that no four consecutive squares in a straight line in any direction (horizontally, vertically, or diagonally) contain more than three of the same symbol.

X		O		O		O	O	O
			X			O	X	O
O		O	X	X			X	O
	X				O		O	
	X		X				O	
		O	O		X			O
X	X		O				O	X
							X	
			O		X			
	O	O			X			O
	O	O			O		X	
	X	X		O			X	O

> "We have only now, only this single eternal moment opening and unfolding before us, day and night."
>
> *Jack Kornfield*

151 Codeword

Every letter in this puzzle has been replaced by a number, the number remaining the same for that letter wherever it occurs. Every letter of the alphabet has been used. Substitute numbers for letters to complete the codeword.

It may help to cross off the letters beneath the grid to keep a track of progress, and to use the reference box showing which numbers have been decoded. Three letters have already been entered into the grid, to help you on your way.

3	2	12	3	1	4	1	13	17		12	26	1	2	11
15		1		21		14		19		26		25		18
26	15	6	2	21		14	15	5	8	15	2	11		1
15		15		17		17		2		21		15		25
11	1	25	2	8	24	10		23	2	22	2	4	13	12
		18		17				15		2				15
21 C	11	15	16		23	1	21	21	2	4	1	26	17	8
1 A		4		24		8		1		13		11		2
25 P	11	17	23	2	15	5	12	24	10		8	2	12	21
1				13		24				9		17		
21	1	8	17	4	20	1		7	24	1	4	4	17	24
2		17		17		26		2		12		4		5
15		2	11	15	4	2	4	13		25	1	2	4	12
5		13		5		15		18		17		1		26
12	15	4	13	12		4	1	26	5	11	1	24	24	10

A B C D E F G H I J K L M
N O P Q R S T U V W X Y Z

1 A	2	3	4	5	6	7	8	9	10	11	12	13
14	15	16	17	18	19	20	21 C	22	23	24	25 P	26

152   **Sudoku**

Place one of the numbers from 1 to 9 into every empty cell so that each row, each column and each 3x3 block contains all the numbers from 1 to 9.

6	1	7			5			
4		8	9	7				3
	2			6		4		5
	9		2	1				
	3	1				8	5	
			3	8			9	
3		6		2			8	
5				8	7	1		2
			4			7	6	9

"If you concentrate on finding whatever is good in every situation, you will discover that your life will suddenly be filled with gratitude, a feeling that nurtures the soul."

Rabbi Harold Kushner

153   Coin Collecting

In this puzzle, an amateur coin collector has been out with his metal detector, searching for booty. He didn't have time to dig up all the coins he found, so has made a grid map, showing their locations, in the hope that if he loses the map, at least no-one else will understand it…

Those squares containing numbers are empty, but where a number appears in a square, it indicates how many coins are located in the squares (up to a maximum of eight) surrounding the numbered one, touching it at any corner or side. There is only one coin in any individual square.

Place a circle into every square containing a coin.

						2		2	
	0	1			3	4		3	
	0		1					4	
			1						2
2							3	2	
		4				2	3		
2			0						
2			2	1		3	4	4	
							3		
	2	1	2			3		2	

"Mindful and creative, a child who has neither a past, nor examples to follow, nor value judgments, simply lives, speaks and plays in freedom."

Arnaud Desjardins

Wordsearch: "U" Words

Can you find all of the listed words that begin with the letter "U" hidden in the grid below? Words run forward or backward, in either a horizontal, vertical or diagonal direction.

U	N	U	W	O	H	N	U	G	L	I	E	R
O	R	T	S	I	N	O	I	N	U	C	H	T
U	O	E	N	I	R	A	M	A	R	T	L	U
G	B	Q	U	U	D	U	M	B	E	R	U	D
A	N	R	N	V	I	U	D	S	F	K	S	O
N	U	D	E	C	N	A	L	A	B	N	U	A
D	R	R	A	H	I	I	R	S	U	U	R	I
A	Y	Q	S	B	S	A	U	E	U	U	P	P
U	A	C	Y	N	N	U	L	D	T	Z	R	O
T	U	Y	E	L	B	A	N	U	D	S	L	T
I	G	T	U	U	L	L	A	G	E	E	L	U
L	U	Y	P	U	I	J	J	W	D	Z	R	U
I	R	P	M	F	V	C	U	T	H	M	B	M
T	U	D	E	H	S	I	N	I	F	N	U	H
Y	W	U	U	V	A	G	X	U	Q	D	B	U

UDDER	UMBER	URUGUAY
UGANDA	UNABLE	USHER
UGLIER	UNBALANCED	USURP
ULLAGE	UNBORN	UTENSILS
ULNAR	UNEASY	UTILITY
ULSTER	UNFINISHED	UTOPIA
ULTRAMARINE	UNIONIST	

"Mindfulness is so powerful that the fact that it comes out of Buddhism is irrelevant."

Jon Kabat-Zinn

Eliminator

Every oval shape contains a different letter of the alphabet from A to K inclusive. Use the clues to determine their locations. Reference in the clues to 'due' means in any location along the same horizontal or vertical line.

1. The A is due south of (but not next to) the C, which is next to and west of the J.
2. The B is next to and north of the I, which is further east than the K.
3. The D is further south than the E and further east than the F.
4. The G is due east of the I, which is due north of the H.

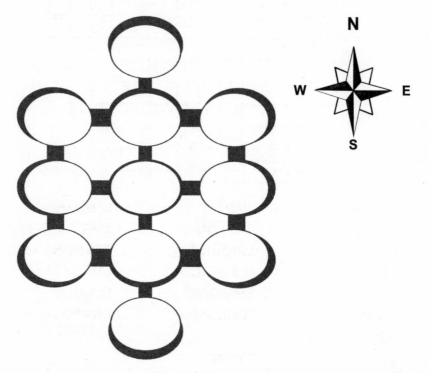

"Mindfulness helps you go home to the present. And every time you go there and recognize a condition of happiness that you have, happiness comes."

Thich Nhất Hanh

156   Criss Cross: Varieties of Apple

The words are provided, but can you fit them all into the grid?

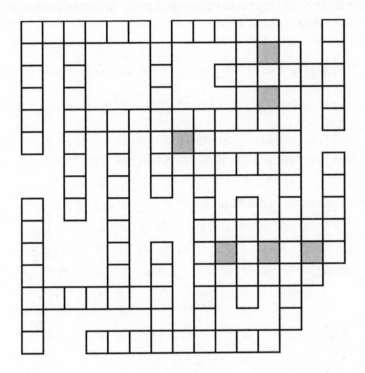

5 letters
AKANE
BRINA
CAMEO
PIXIE
SONYA
TOPAZ

6 letters
BAILEY
ELSTAR
EMPIRE
HAWAII

7 letters
CRISPIN
EPICURE
MONARCH
SPARTAN
WINESAP

9 letters
LIMELIGHT
ROYAL GALA
SWEETANGO

11 letters
SPITZENBERG
TOLMAN SWEET

13 letters
LAXTON'S
SUPERB

Wordsearch: Christmas

Can you find all of the listed words relating to Christmas hidden in the grid below? Words run forward or backward, in either a horizontal, vertical or diagonal direction.

```
S B N P Z X K M A R S H M
C C S S R E J E X P P Q E
R H J N S A E W I M P B Y
O P R O Z O Y C P T A U U
O A O I S X E E A B L D L
G G F T S S C M R E Q C E
E G F A F T V A L G P N T
N I C R I B M O S L O B I
G H S O S H G A A P E Z D
X O E C P T L V S L A M E
S L L E B E I P B E G R L
S W S D O T P A U T V K H
P O I N S E T T I A W E F
J Z T E P S G A K B V E I
X I F Z K U E X A Q M E D
```

BABE	FESTIVAL	POINSETTIA
BELLS	GIFTS	PRAYER
CASPAR	GOLD	SCROOGE
CHRISTMAS EVE	GOOSE	SPICES
	JOSEPH	STABLE
CRIB	NOEL	YULE LOG
DECORATIONS	PEACE	YULETIDE

"What day is it?" asked Pooh.
"It's today," squeaked Piglet.
"My favourite day," said Pooh.

AA Milne

158   Codeword

Every letter in this puzzle has been replaced by a number, the number remaining the same for that letter wherever it occurs. Every letter of the alphabet has been used. Substitute numbers for letters to complete the codeword.

It may help to cross off the letters beneath the grid to keep a track of progress, and to use the reference box showing which numbers have been decoded. Three letters have already been entered into the grid, to help you on your way.

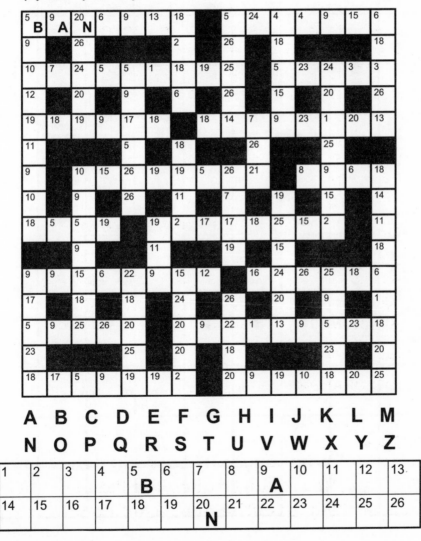

| A | B | C | D | E | F | G | H | I | J | K | L | M |
| N | O | P | Q | R | S | T | U | V | W | X | Y | Z |

1	2	3	4	5 **B**	6	7	8	9 **A**	10	11	12	13.
14	15	16	17	18	19	20 **N**	21	22	23	24	25	26

159 Arroword

Solve the clues, then enter each answer in the direction of the arrows, one letter per square.

Augur	Secretly or unobtrusively (coll) (2,3,5)	Mature female deer	▼	Say again, repeat	Enter unlawfully onto someone's property	Remove forcibly (3,3)	▼	African republic, capital Bamako
▶	▼	▼		Device used to catch animals ▶	▼	▼		
Breathing hole ▶								Utter obscenities or profanities (coll) ▼
▶				Heroic ▶				
Printing command to ignore a former deletion		Likewise ▶					Member of a nomadic tribe of Arabs	
▶				Taverns ▶			▼	
Compass point at 270 degrees		Fills with optimism ▶						
Measurable extent, eg height or breadth		Fourth planet from the Sun	Jacob's biblical twin	Information reported in the papers		Eric ___, member of the Monty Python team		Necessitate
▶	▼	▼	▼	▼		▼		▼
Facilitate ▶					Owing ▶			
▶					False statement ▶			
Cornstalks	Dangle ▶							

160   **Sudoku**

Place one of the numbers from 1 to 9 into every empty cell so that each row, each column and each 3x3 block contains all the numbers from 1 to 9.

2			8			4	7	
		5	6	7			1	
3		4			5			6
			7	4		3	8	9
		1				5		
4	3	9		2	8			
9			1			6		8
	2			3	6	9		
	5	7			2			4

"The moment one gives close attention to anything, even a blade of grass, it becomes a mysterious, awesome, indescribably magnificent world in itself."

Henry Miller

161 Domino Placement

A standard set of twenty-eight dominoes has been laid out as shown below. Can you draw in the edges of them all?

It may be helpful to use the check-box to tick off the dominoes as they are found.

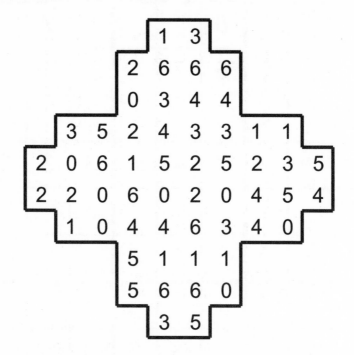

0-0	0-1	0-2	0-3	0-4	0-5	0-6	1-1

1-2	1-3	1-4	1-5	1-6	2-2	2-3	2-4	2-5	2-6

3-3	3-4	3-5	3-6	4-4	4-5	4-6	5-5	5-6	6-6

Can you find all of the listed words relating to watches hidden in the grid below? Words run forward or backward, in either a horizontal, vertical or diagonal direction.

```
O G W M E N I A H C C A R
H J D C I O Q F F Z H E S
P R A F I N K I N E T I C
A F E I Z Z U A H N Q P Z
R L X V S T X T U P K E L
G A U F E I S H E H B N U
O T C W Q L E H R H R D E
N S D I U L S Q I F A A T
O Y J N A X R M N E C N F
R R U D R S U B G G E T D
H C D E T O N Z W N L Z L
C Q I R Z G U Q A I E H F
X L A T I G I D T V T T O
C P L S O U F Q C I Q E B
T E K C O P U A H D F A C
```

BRACELET	DIVING	NURSE'S
CHAIN	FACE	PENDANT
CHRONO- GRAPH	FOB	POCKET
	HUNTER	QUARTZ
CRYSTAL	KINETIC	RING WATCH
DIAL	LEVER	STRAP
DIGITAL	MINUTE HAND	WINDER

"If the doors of perception were cleansed, everything would appear to man as it is, infinite."

William Blake

The words are provided, but can you fit them all into the grid?

3 letters
VET

4 letters
POET

5 letters
BOSUN
CARER
CLERK
CLOWN
TILER

6 letters
BARBER
DRAPER
EDITOR
LAWYER
SINGER
WELDER

7 letters
BAILIFF
DENTIST
PAINTER

8 letters
STITCHER

9 letters
INNKEEPER
PLASTERER

10 letters
CONSULTANT
UNDERTAKER

11 letters
ELECTRICIAN
ROAD SWEEPER

164   Number Cruncher

Starting at the top left with the number provided, work down from one box to another, applying the mathematical instructions to your running total.

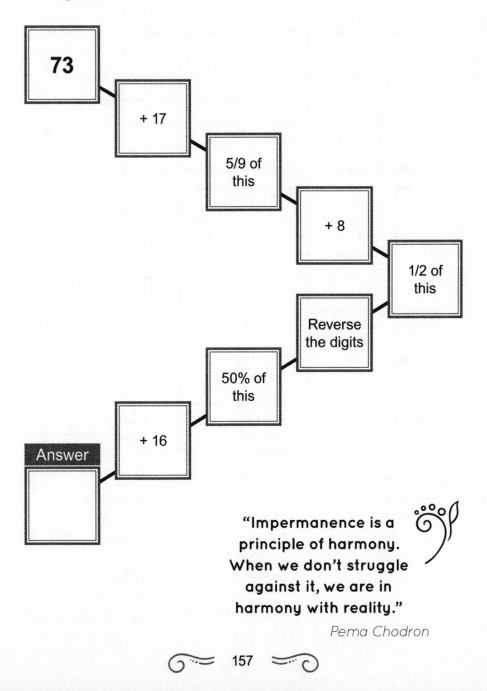

73

+ 17

5/9 of this

+ 8

1/2 of this

Reverse the digits

50% of this

+ 16

Answer

"Impermanence is a principle of harmony. When we don't struggle against it, we are in harmony with reality."

Pema Chodron

Sudoku

Place one of the numbers from 1 to 9 into every empty cell so that each row, each column and each 3x3 block contains all the numbers from 1 to 9.

5			3	4		9		
3	6				7		5	
	2		9			8		1
			6	9		4	2	5
8								7
4	5	6		2	1			
2		1			6		9	
	3		8				4	2
		7		1	3			8

"Between stimulus and response there is a space. In that space is our power to choose our response. In our response lies our growth and our freedom."

Victor Frankl

166   Codeword

Every letter in this puzzle has been replaced by a number, the number remaining the same for that letter wherever it occurs. Every letter of the alphabet has been used. Substitute numbers for letters to complete the codeword.

It may help to cross off the letters beneath the grid to keep a track of progress, and to use the reference box showing which numbers have been decoded. Three letters have already been entered into the grid, to help you on your way.

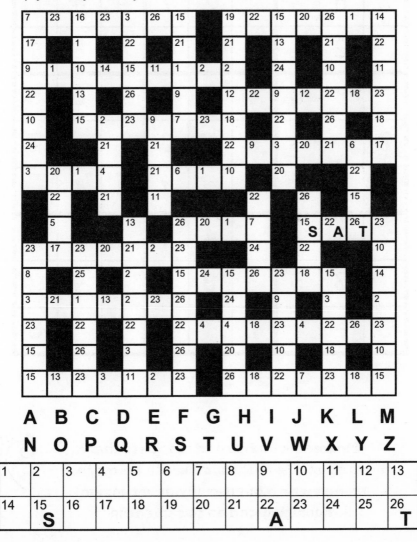

7	23	16	23	3	26	15		19	22	15	20	26	1	14
17		1		22		21		21		13		21		22
9	1	10	14	15	11	1	2	2		24		10		11
22		13		26		9		12	22	9	12	22	18	23
10		15	2	23	9	7	23	18		22		26		18
24			21		21			22	9	3	20	21	6	17
3	20	1	4		21	6	1	10		20			22	
	22		21		11			22		26		15	
	5			13		26	20	1	7		15	22	26	23
											S	A	T	
23	17	23	20	21	2	23			24		22			10
8		25		2		15	24	15	26	23	18	15		14
3	21	1	13	2	23	26		24		9		3		2
23		22		22		22	4	4	18	23	4	22	26	23
15		26		3		26		20		10		18		10
15	13	23	3	11	2	23		26	18	22	7	23	18	15

A B C D E F G H I J K L M

N O P Q R S T U V W X Y Z

1	2	3	4	5	6	7	8	9	10	11	12	13
14	15 **S**	16	17	18	19	20	21	22 **A**	23	24	25	26 **T**

167   Sudoku

Place one of the numbers from 1 to 9 into every empty cell so that each row, each column and each 3x3 block contains all the numbers from 1 to 9.

9			1		4			6
	5	3		2		9	4	
	6			3			8	
	3	8	4		2	7	6	
7			3		8			4
	2	4	9		7	3	1	
	1			4			7	
	7	5		8		4	9	
3			7		1			5

"It takes a little bit of mindfulness and a little bit of attention to others to be a good listener, which helps cultivate emotional nurturing and engagement."

Deepak Chopra

Card Game

Using the playing cards below, can you make five hands each containing three different cards with values that total eleven?

The ace has a value of one.

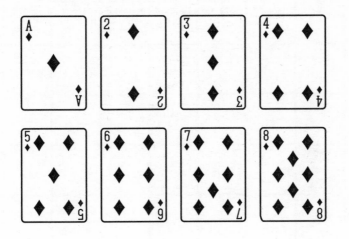

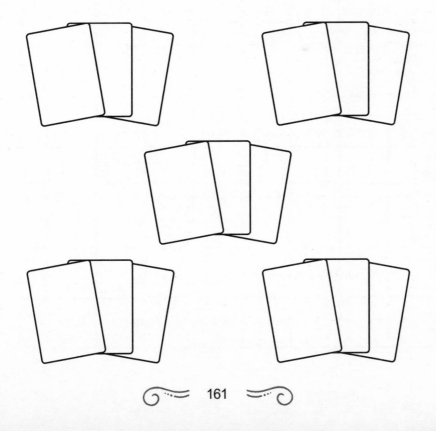

169   **Arroword**

Solve the clues, then enter each answer in the direction of the arrows, one letter per square.

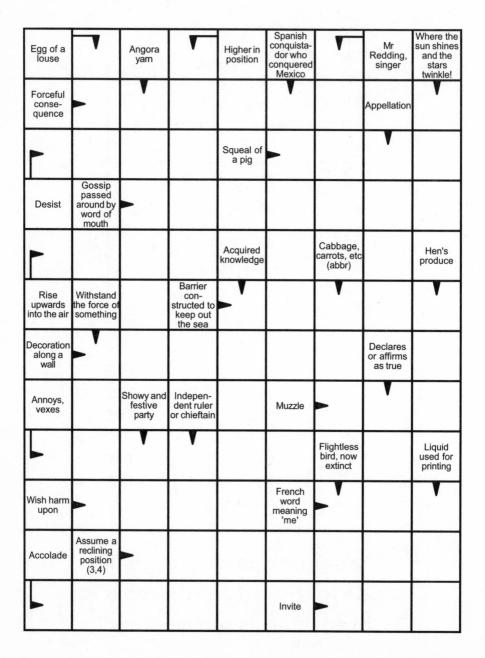

Egg of a louse	▼	Angora yarn	▼	Higher in position	Spanish conquistador who conquered Mexico	▼	Mr Redding, singer	Where the sun shines and the stars twinkle!
Forceful consequence ►		▼					Appellation	▼
►				Squeal of a pig ►			▼	
Desist	Gossip passed around by word of mouth ►							
►				Acquired knowledge		Cabbage, carrots, etc (abbr)		Hen's produce
Rise upwards into the air	Withstand the force of something		Barrier constructed to keep out the sea ►	▼		▼		▼
Decoration along a wall ►	▼						Declares or affirms as true	
Annoys, vexes		Showy and festive party	Independent ruler or chieftain		Muzzle ►		▼	
►		▼	▼			Flightless bird, now extinct		Liquid used for printing
Wish harm upon ►					French word meaning 'me'	▼		▼
Accolade	Assume a reclining position (3,4) ►							
►					Invite ►			

Wordsearch: "T" Words

Can you find all of the listed words that begin with the letter "T" hidden in the grid below? Words run forward or backward, in either a horizontal, vertical or diagonal direction.

Z	A	P	O	T	I	N	D	O	O	T	J	T
P	R	Z	P	E	A	E	E	T	E	A	B	D
S	G	T	G	M	Z	T	L	X	O	W	L	G
D	E	T	C	N	K	D	T	G	T	D	Q	V
T	H	V	G	T	L	U	I	Y	E	R	A	T
T	Y	Q	L	D	R	D	T	E	P	Y	U	Y
V	C	N	R	E	T	U	T	V	I	E	N	V
U	T	Z	O	K	S	W	T	T	D	O	T	J
T	T	T	B	C	E	M	I	H	I	V	R	Z
A	M	A	Y	U	T	X	E	T	F	V	E	Z
F	E	X	U	T	S	N	I	H	C	U	B	F
F	U	I	H	R	E	D	O	E	T	H	L	I
E	G	N	I	S	A	E	T	A	B	L	E	C
T	T	G	Y	R	N	N	O	O	H	P	Y	T
A	B	Y	T	Y	Y	H	S	A	R	T	A	T

TABLE	TEXTURE	TREBLE
TAFFETA	THEMSELVES	TRUTHFUL
TATTY	TITLED	TSETSE
TAWDRY	TODAY	TUCKED
TAXING	TOPAZ	TWITCH
TEASING	TRADITION	TYPHOON
TEPID	TRASHY	

"Feelings come and go like clouds in a windy sky. Conscious breathing is my anchor."

Thich Nhat Hanh

171   **Maze**

Find a path from one circle to the other through this maze.

Criss Cross: Containers

The words are provided, but can you fit them all into the grid?

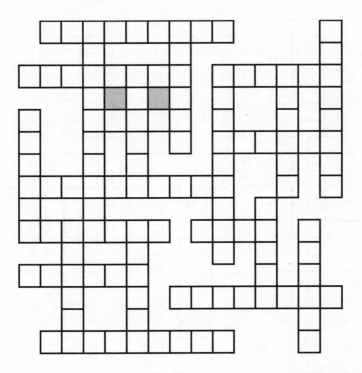

4 letters
BOWL

5 letters
GLASS
PURSE

6 letters
BUNKER
FLAGON
GOBLET
HOPPER
IN-TRAY

MANGER
PARCEL
PUNNET
TIN CAN
WALLET

7 letters
RAMEKIN

8 letters
CANISTER
RUCKSACK
SAUCEPAN

9 letters
FLOWERPOT
GRAVY BOAT
STRONGBOX

10 letters
PERCOLATOR
RECEPTACLE

Solutions

1

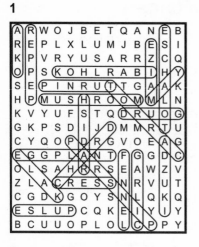

2

A R W O J B E T Q A N E B
R E P L X L U M J B E S I
K P V R Y U S A R R Z C Q
O P S K O H L R A B I H Y
S E P I N R U T T G A A K
H P M U S H R O O M M L N
K V Y U F S T Q D R U O G
G K P S D I J D M M R T U
C Y Q O P D R G V O E A G
E G G P L A N T F G G D C
O L S A H R R S E A W Z V
Z L A C R E S S N R V U T
C G D K G O Y S N L Q K Q
E S L U P C Q K E I Y J Y
B C U U O P L O L C P P Y

	I		S		V		P	
I	N	S	C	R	I	B	E	S
	T	O	Y		T	U	N	E
R	E	S	T	R	A	I	N	T
	R		H	A	M	L	E	T
I	N	H	E	R	I	T		O
	E	D	E	N		T		
I	R	A			S	L	A	B
	O	R	S	O		A	G	E
S	O	D	A	W	A	T	E	R
	M		F	L	Y	I	N	G
B	Y	R	E		E	N	D	S

3

4

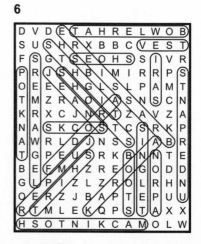

5

6

Solutions

7

7	6	8	2	9	5	4	3	1
9	2	1	4	6	3	8	5	7
3	4	5	1	7	8	9	6	2
4	9	3	7	2	1	5	8	6
5	8	2	9	3	6	7	1	4
1	7	6	5	8	4	2	9	3
6	3	9	8	4	7	1	2	5
8	1	7	3	5	2	6	4	9
2	5	4	6	1	9	3	7	8

8

B

9

The nine-letter word is:
SWEETCORN

10

The value of the central letter is the total value of the letters in the top right, top left and bottom right squares, minus the value of the letter in the bottom left square. Thus the missing value is 9, so the missing letter is I.

11

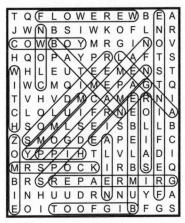

12

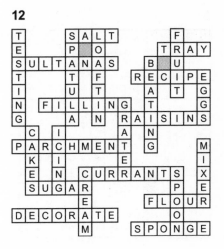

13

	M		B		H		
R	E	M	O	R	S	E		T
	A			A	O	R	T	A
S	T	O	N	E	D	E	A	D
		I			A		C	
V	I	L	L	A		B	O	B
	M		E	T	U	I		O
A	B	E	A	M		G	I	G
	U		P		C		G	
W	E	E	D		U	G	L	I
		B	A	L	L	O	O	N
B	A	B	Y		M	O	O	N

14

9

Add the numbers in the corresponding squares of the top right and bottom left sets to obtain the numbers in the corresponding squares in the central set.

15

304 ÷ 8 = 38
965 + 659 = 1624
283 − 46 = 237
57 x 7 = 399
(21 x 6) − 17 = 109

Solutions

16

S	Q	U	I	R	E		S	T	U	M	B	L	E	D
H			K		M			H		A		I		Y
I	N	T	E	R	P	O	S	E		N		D		S
P			B		O		O	M	N	I	V	O	R	E
S	A	G	A		R	I	D			F			E	N
	I		N		I		A	P	S	E		Z		T
A	L	M	A	N	A	C		U		S	I	E	V	E
V		I		E		H	U	M		T		R		R
A	G	L	O	W		E		A	P	O	L	O	G	Y
I			E		C	O	W	S		E		I		U
L			O			E	A	R		G	A	M	E
A	S	S	E	M	B	L	E		J		H		D
B			L		E		I	N	S	U	L	T	I	N	G
L			A		R		E		R		E		E
E	X	P	O	S	I	N	G		Y	A	N	K	E	D

17

18

5	8	4	9	2	7	3	6	1
2	7	6	4	3	1	8	5	9
9	1	3	5	8	6	7	4	2
4	9	2	8	7	5	1	3	6
8	6	5	1	4	3	9	2	7
7	3	1	2	6	9	5	8	4
6	5	8	7	1	2	4	9	3
3	4	7	6	9	8	2	1	5
1	2	9	3	5	4	6	7	8

19

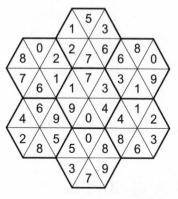

20

27	40	6	19	35	15	21	40
18	12	14	4	11	16	9	13
24	8	1	8	38	10	12	37
19	35	33	27	3	25	14	4
38	29	33	34	6	19	15	28
15	25	34	33	34	12	38	29
39	36	5	30	12	13	31	22
10	30	38	2	35	16	10	6

21

232 − 34 = 198, 198 ÷ 2 = 99, 99 ÷ 9 x 5 = 55, 55 ÷ 11 x 4 = 20, 20 + 19 = 39, 39 ÷ 3 x 2 = 26, 26 + 42 = 68

Solutions

22

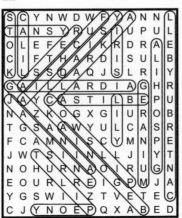

23

7	3	5	1	2	9	8	4	6
8	2	4	3	6	5	9	1	7
9	1	6	4	7	8	2	5	3
6	7	3	5	8	4	1	9	2
4	9	2	6	3	1	7	8	5
1	5	8	2	9	7	6	3	4
3	8	7	9	5	2	4	6	1
5	4	9	7	1	6	3	2	8
2	6	1	8	4	3	5	7	9

24

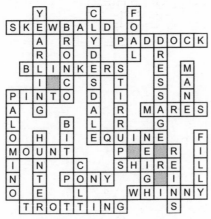

25

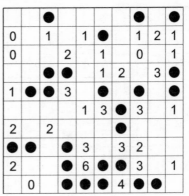

26

27

9	3	1	7	4	8	5	6	2
4	8	5	2	6	9	3	1	7
2	7	6	5	3	1	8	9	4
1	5	2	4	7	3	9	8	6
3	4	9	6	8	2	1	7	5
8	6	7	9	1	5	4	2	3
7	1	4	8	5	6	2	3	9
5	9	8	3	2	7	6	4	1
6	2	3	1	9	4	7	5	8

Solutions

28

	E	G		G			
F	A	U	N	A		A	C	E
	R		R	U	N	I	N
C	R	O	W	D		G	A	Y
	O		O	A	F	S		A
D	E	C	K		I	T	S
	R		D	R	E	A	D
A	B	A	S	E		R	Y	E
	I	N	T	R	O		L
G	R	I	E	V	A	N	C	E
	C	U	P		T	O	O	T
O	H	M		T	H	R	O	E

29

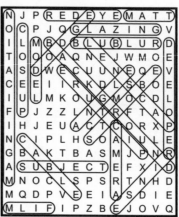

30

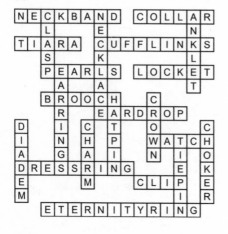

31

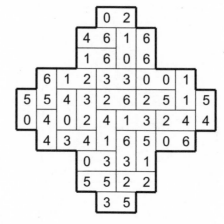

32

33

3	4	9	5	6	1	2	7	8
1	7	5	8	2	9	3	4	6
2	6	8	3	7	4	1	5	9
8	3	4	2	9	6	7	1	5
6	5	2	1	8	7	9	3	4
9	1	7	4	5	3	6	8	2
7	9	1	6	4	8	5	2	3
4	2	3	9	1	5	8	6	7
5	8	6	7	3	2	4	9	1

Solutions

34

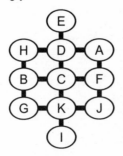

35

36

37

	E		Q		A		D	
	S	A	U	C	E	P	A	N
A	P	S	E		R		S	
		S	L	E	I	G	H	T
	P	I	L	L	A	R		O
		G		F	L	A	C	K
P	E	N	S			C	O	Y
	N		T		M	E	M	O
J	A	B	O	T			B	
	B	O	A		S	P	I	T
	L	O	T		T	U	N	E
B	E	N		T	Y	P	E	D

38

39

82 – 39 = 43, 43 x 2 = 86, 86 – 18
= 68, 68 x 2 = 136, 25% of 136 =
34, 34 – 14 = 20, 20 x 70 = 1400

Solutions

40

6	1	7	8	5	3	9	2	4
2	5	9	6	4	1	3	7	8
4	8	3	9	2	7	5	1	6
3	6	5	7	8	4	1	9	2
7	4	2	3	1	9	8	6	5
1	9	8	5	6	2	7	4	3
5	7	1	4	3	6	2	8	9
8	2	6	1	9	5	4	3	7
9	3	4	2	7	8	6	5	1

41

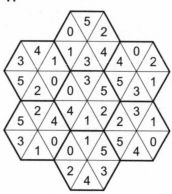

42

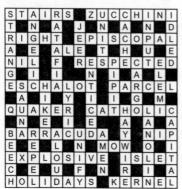

43

24	17	40	25	15	17	30	19
23	6	13	26	21	29	38	11
32	17	27	22	12	2	10	6
31	22	33	10	18	25	36	39
12	29	8	17	36	28	31	23
1	9	9	27	15	29	12	13
39	24	24	21	20	30	3	14
2	37	17	13	31	23	36	23

44

7	5	9	1	2	4	8	6	3
6	4	1	8	5	3	7	9	2
8	3	2	9	6	7	1	5	4
9	6	5	7	3	8	4	2	1
2	8	4	6	9	1	3	7	5
3	1	7	2	4	5	9	8	6
4	7	8	5	1	6	2	3	9
5	9	3	4	7	2	6	1	8
1	2	6	3	8	9	5	4	7

45

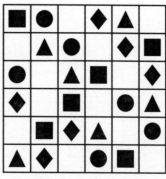

Solutions

46

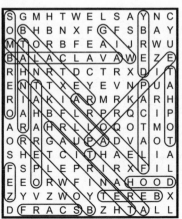

47

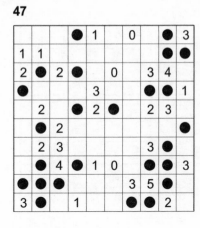

48

R U S H D I E   B E C K E T T

49

X	O	O	O	X	X	X	O	O
O	O	X	X	X	O	O	O	X
X	X	X	O	X	X	X	O	X
X	O	O	X	O	X	O	X	O
O	O	X	O	X	O	O	O	X
X	O	O	O	X	O	X	X	O
O	X	X	O	O	X	O	O	X
O	X	O	X	X	O	X	X	X
X	X	X	O	X	X	X	O	O
X	O	O	X	X	O	O	X	O
O	X	X	O	O	O	X	O	X
O	O	X	O	X	X	X	O	O

50

FOOL – wool – wood – word –
wore – wire – WISE
(Other solutions are possible)

51

The nine-letter word is:
ANSWERING

Solutions

52

O	U	T	B	I	D	■	Z	■	E	F	F	E	C	T
T	■	O	■	U	N	I	O	N	■	A	■	H	■	
H	E	R	O	I	C	■	N	■	J	■	I	■	I	
E	■	Q	■	A	■	G	R	O	W	L	I	N	G	
R	■	U	■	P	L	O	Y	■	Y	■	T	■	R	
■	V	E	T	O	■	U	■	D	■	S	I	E	G	E
E	■	■	L	A	T	T	I	C	E	■	M	■	A	
M	U	F	T	I	■	C	■	N	■	T	U	S	K	S
E	■	U	■	C	O	R	O	N	E	T	■	■	Y	
T	O	D	A	Y	■	Y	■	E	■	E	N	V	Y	
I	■	G	■	A	■	T	R	E	E	■	E	■	T	
C	R	E	D	I	T	O	R	■	N	■	X	■	H	
■	O	■	I	■	L	■	A	■	D	O	M	I	N	O
■	T	■	N	■	A	N	I	S	E	■	N	■	R	
T	A	P	E	R	S	■	T	■	D	R	A	G	O	N

53

■	R	■	■	O	■	N	■	■
■	A	R	C	H	■	I	■	N	N
■	Y	E	O	M	A	N	■	■	O
A	S	P	S	■	E	A	T
■	■	T	H	I	S	T	L	E
■	■	I	■	K	■	Y	O	D
H	A	L	V	E	D	■	H
■	T	E	E	■	■	C	A	P
■	T	■	N	I	N	E	■	I
R	I	S	E	N	■	L	I	S
■	R	■	E	F	F	E	C	T
M	E	T	R	O	■	B	Y	E

54

1	3	8	4	9	2	5	6	7
6	4	7	5	3	1	9	2	8
9	5	2	6	8	7	3	4	1
5	1	9	7	6	3	2	8	4
2	7	6	9	4	8	1	5	3
4	8	3	1	2	5	6	7	9
3	2	4	8	1	6	7	9	5
7	9	1	2	5	4	8	3	6
8	6	5	3	7	9	4	1	2

55

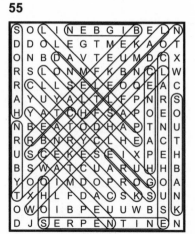

56

57

3	2	4	6	9	5	7	8	1
5	7	6	3	8	1	4	9	2
1	8	9	7	2	4	3	6	5
6	1	8	9	5	3	2	4	7
9	3	5	4	7	2	8	1	6
7	4	2	1	6	8	5	3	9
4	9	1	5	3	7	6	2	8
2	5	3	8	1	6	9	7	4
8	6	7	2	4	9	1	5	3

Solutions

58

59

60

6	4	8	2	1	7	5	9	3
9	2	7	5	3	8	6	4	1
5	1	3	9	6	4	2	8	7
2	3	6	8	5	9	1	7	4
8	5	1	4	7	6	3	2	9
7	9	4	3	2	1	8	5	6
1	8	2	7	4	3	9	6	5
4	6	5	1	9	2	7	3	8
3	7	9	6	8	5	4	1	2

61

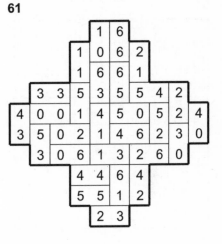

62

63

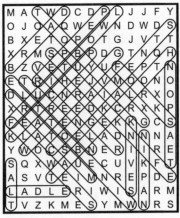

Solutions

64

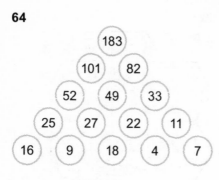

65

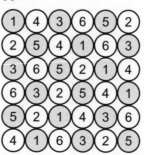

66

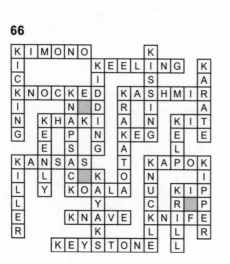

67

68

69

B – Starting at the top left number and working clockwise, subtract the next number, add the next number and continue likewise until you arrive at 20 in the centre.

70

Solutions

71

9	6	8	4	1	2	3	5	7
4	5	7	3	9	8	6	1	2
2	3	1	5	7	6	4	9	8
3	2	4	9	6	5	8	7	1
1	8	9	2	3	7	5	4	6
5	7	6	1	8	4	2	3	9
8	9	5	6	4	1	7	2	3
7	4	3	8	2	9	1	6	5
6	1	2	7	5	3	9	8	4

72

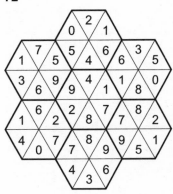

73

33	11	37	15	23	21	22	2
21	18	9	31	23	13	13	39
32	35	25	36	24	11	21	19
6	33	29	31	27	16	26	18
38	24	39	32	18	22	17	23
23	3	8	15	33	11	10	28
22	9	20	29	22	19	12	28
13	12	35	24	38	39	29	31

74

```
B K P F A N N A O J   J W K
O D I V A D O N Y U E W O
A R R Z Z N H R E R J F F
Z P A R R O I Y A I D E U
B Q V X J X I X S A Z O B
F I R T A L C H N H Y J K
C Y R U S E A J W M A R Y
R A O E G C L B B Q N Q Y
O X R E H O B O A M O E D
L D Y U S C Q H B N E O K
P E H O S E A W E R D N A
Q N A U U F N N C A I J L
S H W J I M O A N Q G K A
V J E Z E B E L X E J O B
R P F X Z V M O L A S B A
```

75

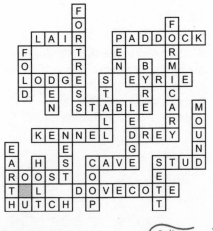

76

	N	M	N		K			
A	U	T	O	M	A	T	O	N
	T	O	N		T	A	R	O
I	R	R	E	G	U	L	A	R
	I	C	Y		R	U	N	T
B	A	H		W	A	S		H
		B	O	I	L		J	
C	L	E	F	T		P	E	R
	E	A	T		N	A	S	A
B	A	R		B	O	S	U	N
	S	E	M	A	N	T	I	C
H	E	R		T	E	E	T	H

Solutions

77

3	2	6	5	1	8	4	9	7
8	1	7	4	9	6	3	2	5
4	9	5	3	2	7	6	1	8
6	4	9	1	8	2	7	5	3
7	8	3	6	5	9	1	4	2
1	5	2	7	3	4	8	6	9
5	3	4	2	7	1	9	8	6
2	6	8	9	4	3	5	7	1
9	7	1	8	6	5	2	3	4

78

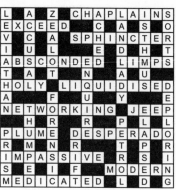

79

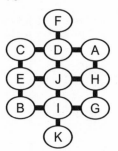

80

8	2	6	1	4	5	9	7	3
9	7	1	2	3	6	5	8	4
4	3	5	8	9	7	6	1	2
5	4	2	3	6	1	8	9	7
1	6	3	7	8	9	2	4	5
7	9	8	5	2	4	3	6	1
3	5	7	6	1	8	4	2	9
2	8	4	9	7	3	1	5	6
6	1	9	4	5	2	7	3	8

81

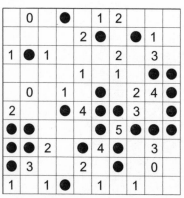

82

6 + 8 = 14, 14 ÷ 7 = 2, 2 + 47 = 49, 49 ÷ 7 = 7, 7 + 2 = 9, 9 ÷ 3 = 3, 3 + 68 = 71

83

E

Solutions

84

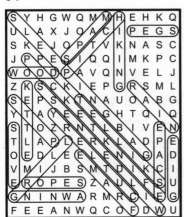

85

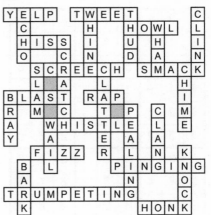

86

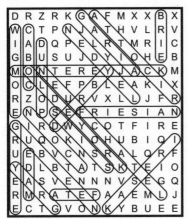

87

C	F	D	E	A	B
D	A	B	C	E	F
A	B	C	F	D	E
F	C	E	A	B	D
E	D	A	B	F	C
B	E	F	D	C	A

88

8646

In all the other numbers the first and last digits are multiplied together to obtain the number that is the middle two digits.

89

90

	W		W	H	
	A	B	L	E		A	I	L
	G	A	I	T	E	R		A
H	E	N	S			D	A	M
		S	T	A	T	U	R	E
		H		V		P	O	D
P	E	E	L	E	D		M	
	L	E	I			B	A	P
	D		N	O	D	E		H
M	E	T	E	D		T	W	A
	S		U	D	D	E	R	S
S	T	E	P	S		L	Y	E

Solutions

91

1	8	2	7	3	9	4	6	5
6	4	3	5	1	8	7	9	2
5	9	7	6	2	4	1	3	8
7	1	5	2	8	6	3	4	9
4	2	6	9	7	3	8	5	1
8	3	9	1	4	5	2	7	6
3	6	8	4	9	1	5	2	7
9	7	4	8	5	2	6	1	3
2	5	1	3	6	7	9	8	4

92

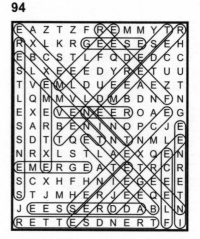

93

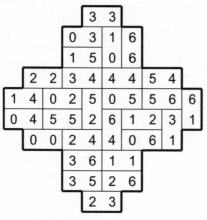

94

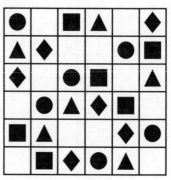

95

96

The value of the central letter is the total value of the two letters in the highest boxes and also the total value of the two letters in the lowest boxes. Thus the missing value is 18, so the missing letter is R.

97

HIDE – bide – bids – beds – bees – sees – SEEK
(Other solutions are possible)

Solutions

98

8	1	2	4	6	9	7	5	3
6	3	7	2	5	8	1	9	4
5	4	9	1	3	7	6	2	8
7	5	6	3	9	1	4	8	2
9	2	3	7	8	4	5	1	6
1	8	4	6	2	5	3	7	9
4	6	1	8	7	2	9	3	5
3	9	8	5	1	6	2	4	7
2	7	5	9	4	3	8	6	1

99

A, F and H
B, D and J
C, G and K
E, I and L

100

101

102

O	X	O	X	X	X	O	O	X
O	O	X	X	X	O	O	X	X
X	X	X	O	O	O	X	O	O
O	O	O	X	X	O	X	O	O
O	X	X	O	X	X	X	O	X
X	X	O	X	O	O	O	X	O
O	X	O	O	X	X	X	O	X
X	O	X	X	X	O	O	O	X
O	X	X	O	O	X	X	X	O
X	O	O	X	O	O	O	X	O
O	X	O	X	O	X	X	X	O
O	O	O	X	X	X	O	O	X

103

6	2	8	4	1	3	5	9	7
9	5	4	8	6	7	1	2	3
3	7	1	9	2	5	6	8	4
7	3	2	1	8	4	9	6	5
1	4	9	6	5	2	7	3	8
8	6	5	7	3	9	4	1	2
2	9	6	5	7	8	3	4	1
5	1	3	2	4	6	8	7	9
4	8	7	3	9	1	2	5	6

Solutions

104

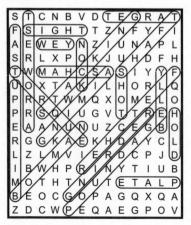

105

	S		M			F		
	A	R	O	U	S	E		S
A	G	E	S		P	E	S	O
		A	E	R	O	S	O	L
A	I	D	S		I		B	
		E		U	L	C	E	R
	P	R	E	S	S	U	R	E
	E			E		R		L
M	E	L	O	D	R	A	M	A
	R	O	B		A	T	O	P
		P	O	M	P	O	U	S
F	L	E	E		T	R	E	E

106

F

107

108

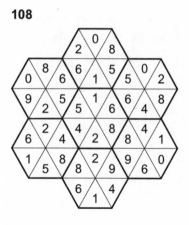

109

110

22	4	9	10	36	26	16	32
37	21	36	19	27	18	30	1
28	28	37	28	10	9	10	18
11	26	13	40	18	7	30	18
33	9	20	3	1	18	2	24
25	12	5	8	36	15	1	39
19	7	13	4	35	30	1	29
32	38	6	13	31	30	34	22

Solutions

111

9	1	4	5	2	3	7	6	8
5	7	2	8	6	4	9	1	3
3	6	8	7	9	1	5	4	2
1	5	3	2	4	6	8	9	7
7	2	6	1	8	9	4	3	5
4	8	9	3	5	7	1	2	6
8	3	7	4	1	2	6	5	9
2	9	1	6	7	5	3	8	4
6	4	5	9	3	8	2	7	1

112

The nine-letter word is:
SOVEREIGN

113

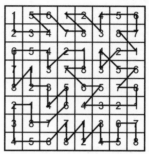

114

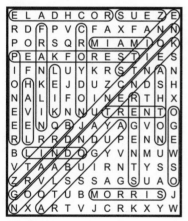

115

3	8	1	5	4	2	6	7	9
4	2	6	8	7	9	3	5	1
7	9	5	6	3	1	2	4	8
1	3	7	2	5	8	4	9	6
9	6	8	4	1	7	5	2	3
5	4	2	9	6	3	1	8	7
2	7	4	1	9	6	8	3	5
8	1	3	7	2	5	9	6	4
6	5	9	3	8	4	7	1	2

116

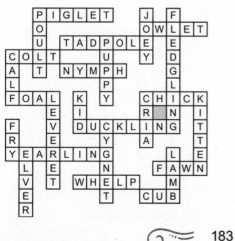

117

The nine-letter word is:
CATHEDRAL

118

BLUE – glue – glut – gout – goat – goad – GOLD
(Other solutions are possible)

Solutions

119

```
  C   S   O   D
  O A T   D R E Y
  U R I   I   F
I N T R I N S I C
  T   T   A L L
  E L S E   L E A
  R E A M   V   S
S P E W   C O G S
  O   D U O   R
  I O U   S P U N
  S   S E T T E E
T E N T   S A L T
```

120

121

4	3	6	5	2	9	7	1	8
8	5	1	4	6	7	2	9	3
2	7	9	1	3	8	6	5	4
5	1	3	8	9	6	4	7	2
9	8	2	7	4	5	3	6	1
6	4	7	2	1	3	5	8	9
3	6	8	9	5	4	1	2	7
7	2	4	6	8	1	9	3	5
1	9	5	3	7	2	8	4	6

122

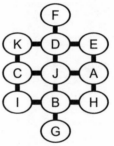

123

●	2			0		0		2	●
2	●			2	1		2	●	
		●	●	●	2		●	3	
0		2				●		●	2
		1		2		1	3	●	
●			●	●			3	4	3
●	2	1		2		●	●	●	
		0		●	3	3	●		
0				●	3	3		2	
	●	2	●		●	2	●		

124

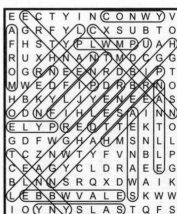

Solutions

125

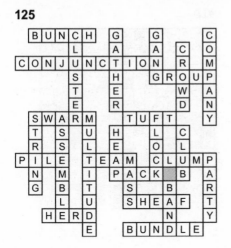

126

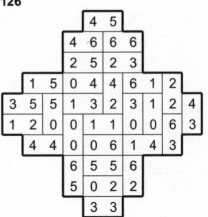

127

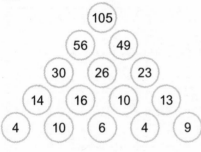

128

U
Assign values to the letters, working in alphabetical order, A = 1, B = 2, etc, to Z = 26:
18 (R) ÷ 9 (I) = 2 (B)
2 (B) + 10 (J) = 12 (L)
16 (P) − 5 (E) = 11 (K)
7 (G) x 3 (C) = 21 (U)

129

57 + 17 = 74, 74 ÷ 2 = 37, 37 + 19 = 56, 56 ÷ 4 = 14, 14 reversed = 41, 41 + 55 = 96, 25% of 96 = 24

130

131

8	5	7	6	4	3	1	9	2
4	2	6	1	9	8	3	5	7
1	9	3	2	7	5	4	8	6
7	1	8	3	6	2	9	4	5
9	4	2	5	1	7	6	3	8
3	6	5	4	8	9	2	7	1
2	3	1	8	5	4	7	6	9
5	7	4	9	2	6	8	1	3
6	8	9	7	3	1	5	2	4

Solutions

132

	T		D		I		B	
	O	R	I	E	N	T	A	L
	F	U	G		F		B	
O	U	R	S	E	L	V	E	S
		A		B	U	I	L	T
	G	L	O	B	E	S		A
	Y			S	N	O	R	T
S	P	R	Y		C	R	E	E
		I			E		C	
M	O	V	I	E	S	T	A	R
	D	E	A	N		A	L	I
	E	R	N	E		O	L	D

133

134

135

1	4	6	3	9	8	2	7	5
3	7	8	6	2	5	1	4	9
2	9	5	4	7	1	3	8	6
6	3	7	1	8	4	9	5	2
9	8	2	7	5	3	6	1	4
5	1	4	9	6	2	7	3	8
7	6	3	5	4	9	8	2	1
4	2	1	8	3	6	5	9	7
8	5	9	2	1	7	4	6	3

136

137

D – Each letter in the top row moves back one place in the alphabet, whilst the others move forward two places in the alphabet every time.

138

Solutions

139

140

1	6	5	8	3	9	7	4	2
7	8	2	5	6	4	3	9	1
3	9	4	7	2	1	8	6	5
4	5	3	1	7	8	9	2	6
8	2	6	9	5	3	4	1	7
9	7	1	2	4	6	5	3	8
6	4	7	3	1	5	2	8	9
2	3	9	6	8	7	1	5	4
5	1	8	4	9	2	6	7	3

141

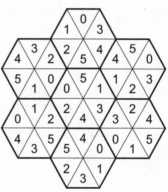

142

5	32	26	36	9	6	24	14
13	30	25	31	29	17	24	13
7	9	31	2	31	31	11	25
29	9	16	2	17	28	22	22
24	23	2	9	33	30	24	2
11	19	15	1	25	39	35	30
21	3	33	38	17	16	37	8
14	25	29	22	32	13	27	26

143

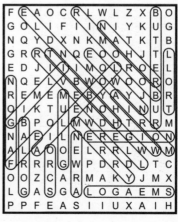

144

G

It has an even number of black
squares/odd number of white
squares: all of the others have an
odd number of black squares/even
number of white squares.

Solutions

145

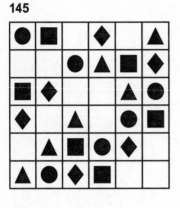

146

The value of the central letter is the total value of the two letters in the highest boxes multiplied by the total value of the two letters in the lowest boxes. Thus the missing value is 1, so the missing letter is A.

147

CURE – lure – lore – lose – lost – lest – REST
(Other solutions are possible)

148

149

	A		A			T
L	A	C	R	O	S	S	E
S	P	O	T		C		P
H	O	R	O	S	C	O	P	E
	O			L	U	R	E
U	N	A	W	A	R	E	S
N		S		U		E
C	R	O	I	S	S	A	N	T
A	P	N	O	E	A		A
V	E	I	L		R	A	N
H	E	N	N	A		O	U	T
L		E	R	Y	N	G	O

150

X	O	O	X	O	X	O	O	O
O	X	X	X	O	X	O	X	O
O	O	O	X	X	O	X	X	O
X	X	O	O	X	O	X	O	X
O	X	X	X	O	O	X	O	O
X	O	O	O	X	X	O	X	O
X	X	X	O	O	O	X	O	X
O	O	O	X	X	X	O	X	X
X	X	X	O	O	X	O	X	O
O	O	O	X	X	X	O	O	O
X	O	O	O	X	O	X	X	X
X	X	X	O	O	O	X	X	O

151

M	I	S	M	A	N	A	G	E		S	T	A	I	R
O		A		C		B		Q		T		P		H
T	O	X	I	C		B	O	U	D	O	I	R		A
O		O		E		E		I		C		O		P
R	A	P	I	D	L	Y		V	I	K	I	N	G	S
		H		E				O		I				O
C	R	O	W		V	A	C	C	I	N	A	T	E	D
A		N		L		D		A		G		R		I
P	R	E	V	I	O	U	S	L	Y		D	I	S	C
A				G		L			J		E			
C	A	D	E	N	Z	A		F	L	A	N	N	E	L
I		E		E		T		I		S		N		U
O		I	R	O	N	I	N	G		P	A	I	N	S
U		G		U		O		H		E		A		T
S	O	N	G	S		N	A	T	U	R	A	L	L	Y

Solutions

152

6	1	7	3	4	5	9	2	8
4	5	8	9	7	2	6	1	3
9	2	3	8	6	1	4	7	5
8	9	5	2	1	6	3	4	7
2	3	1	7	9	4	8	5	6
7	6	4	5	3	8	2	9	1
3	7	6	1	2	9	5	8	4
5	4	9	6	8	7	1	3	2
1	8	2	4	5	3	7	6	9

153

				●	2		2		
	0	1	●		3	4	●	3	●
	0		1		●	●		4	●
				1		●		●	2
2	●	●					3	2	
	●	4				2	3	●	
2	●		0			●	●		●
2			2	1		3	4	4	●
●		●		●			●	3	●
	2	1	2		●	3	●	2	

154

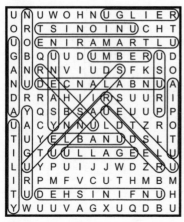

155

```
            F
            |
   C ------ J ------ E
   |        |        |
   K ------ B ------ D
   |        |        |
   A ------ I ------ G
            |
            H
```

156

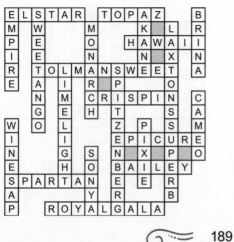

157

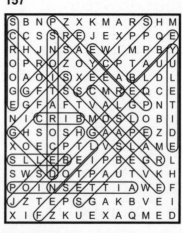

Solutions

B	A	N	D	A	G	E		B	U	Z	Z	A	R	D
A		O		Y		O		E						E
C	H	U	B	B	I	E	S	T		B	L	U	F	F
K		N		A		D		O		R		N		O
S	E	S	A	M	E		E	X	H	A	L	I	N	G
P			B		E			O		T				
A		C	R	O	S	S	B	O	W		J	A	D	E
C		A		O		P		H		S		R		X
E	B	B	S		S	Y	M	M	E	T	R	Y		P
		A		P		S		S		R				E
A	A	R	D	V	A	R	K		Q	U	O	T	E	D
M		E		E		U		O		N		A		I
B	A	T	O	N		N	A	V	I	G	A	B	L	E
L				T		N		E				L		N
E	M	B	A	S	S	Y		N	A	S	C	E	N	T

159

		R				M		
B	O	D	E		T	R	A	P
	N	O	S	T	R	I	L	
S	T	E	T		E	P	I	C
	H		A	L	S	O		U
W	E	S	T		P	U	B	S
	Q		E	L	A	T	E	S
	U			S		D		
D	I	M	E	N	S	I	O	N
	E	A	S	E		D	U	E
S	T	R	A	W		L	I	E
		S	U	S	P	E	N	D

160

2	1	6	8	9	3	4	7	5
8	9	5	6	7	4	2	1	3
3	7	4	2	1	5	8	9	6
5	6	2	7	4	1	3	8	9
7	8	1	3	6	9	5	4	2
4	3	9	5	2	8	7	6	1
9	4	3	1	5	7	6	2	8
1	2	8	4	3	6	9	5	7
6	5	7	9	8	2	1	3	4

161

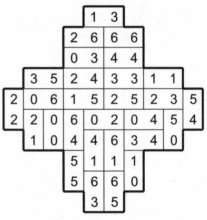

162

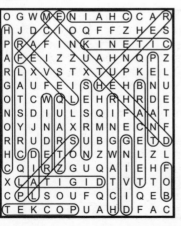

163

Solutions

164

73 + 17 = 90, 90 ÷ 9 x 5 = 50, 50 +
8 = 58, 58 ÷ 2 = 29, 29 reversed =
92, 50% of 92 = 46, 46 + 16 = 62

165

5	1	8	3	4	2	9	7	6
3	6	9	1	8	7	2	5	4
7	2	4	9	6	5	8	3	1
1	7	3	6	9	8	4	2	5
8	9	2	5	3	4	6	1	7
4	5	6	7	2	1	3	8	9
2	8	1	4	5	6	7	9	3
6	3	5	8	7	9	1	4	2
9	4	7	2	1	3	5	6	8

166

167

9	8	2	1	7	4	5	3	6
1	5	3	8	2	6	9	4	7
4	6	7	5	3	9	1	8	2
5	3	8	4	1	2	7	6	9
7	9	1	3	6	8	2	5	4
6	2	4	9	5	7	3	1	8
8	1	9	2	4	5	6	7	3
2	7	5	6	8	3	4	9	1
3	4	6	7	9	1	8	2	5

168

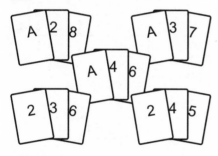

169

170

Solutions

171

172